PRACTISE YOUR LANGUAGE SKILLS

BOOK

4

PRACTISE YOUR LANGUAGE SKILLS

GRAMMAR

WRITING

WORD KNOWLEDGE

SENTENCES

PUNCTUATION

READING

BOOK 4

Peter Howard

Copp Clark Ltd.
Toronto

Cover design: Mary Opper
Cover illustration: Kim LaFave
Typesetting: April Haisell

ISBN 0-7730-5460-X

Copp Clark Ltd.
2775 Matheson Blvd. East
Mississauga, Ontario
L4W 4P7

Printed and bound in Canada
1 2 3 4 5   5460-X   99 98 97 96 95

TABLE OF CONTENTS

Reading: Finding facts

Today Donald and his sister Helen started at a new school in Regina. The children had come from the country. Their old school was very small. All the pupils were crowded into one room. There was only one teacher. The new school had many classrooms. No wonder Donald and Helen felt a little nervous.

Write the two sentences that are true.

1. Donald and Helen now live in Regina.

2. They were used to big schools.

3. Donald and Helen now live in the country.

4. They were not used to big schools.

Word Knowledge: More about school

Match each word from the box to its meaning below. Write each word with its meaning in your notebook.

> chair   blackboard   principal   library
> mathematics   spelling   playground   dictionary
> pencil   ruler   practise   atlas

1. area for playing

2. head of a school

3. Teachers write on it.

4. do again and again

5. We sit on it.

6. We write with it.

7. collection of books

8. book explaining words

9. study of numbers

10. book of maps

11. used for measuring

12. writing or saying the letters of a word in order

Sentences: What are they?

A sentence has a beginning and an end. It must say something sensible. Read the group of words next to each number. They do not make sense by themselves. Use the words from the box to write sensible sentences in your notebook.

purr   jeans   The cat was   leaves
wake up   letters

1. I like writing _____.

2. My cat can _____.

3. Mother wears _____.

4. _____ under the bed.

5. In the morning I _____.

6. The tree had green _____.

Punctuation: Sentences have capitals and periods

A sentence begins with a capital letter and ends with a period. Rewrite these sentences correctly.

1. my horse is lame

2. they went to the beach

3. two ducks swam on the dam

4. the pink flower was pretty

5. she rode on her bicycle

6. he likes singing at school

Grammar: Common nouns

Common nouns are words we use to name ordinary things. These words are not written with a capital letter unless they begin a sentence.

The **boy** sits at his **desk**.   Some **girls** have **books**.

In your notebook, write the sentences using a suitable noun from the box in each space.

```
        fish    Buses    bell    house    apple
        rod     Birds    tree    man      sea
```

1. I picked an ____ from our ____.

2. ____ pass near our ____.

3. ____ can fly.

4. The ____ rang and we came inside.

5. The ____ fished with a ____.

6. Many ____ swim in the ____.

Now circle in red each common noun.

Dictionary Skills: The alphabet

a b c d e f g h i j k l m n o p q r s t u v w x y z

Write the letter that comes after each of the following.

1. f	**3.** p	**5.** x	**7.** j	**9.** a	**11.** s
2. u	**4.** e	**6.** y	**8.** l	**10.** d	**12.** r

Written Expression: Describing myself

Write the sentences and fill the spaces with one or more words.

My name is ____. My hair is ____ and I have ____ eyes. In our family there is/are ____ boy/boys and ____ girl/girls. I live at ____. My best friend is ____. We ____. After school I like ____.

Word Families: 'ill' as in 'will'

----
will   bill   fill   gill   sill

Write new words of the same family from the clues.

1. place where flour is made

3. high ground

2. sold in a drugstore

4. a drawer where money is kept

Just For Fun: Anagrams

Rearrange the letters of each underlined word to make new words.

1. Make <u>gum</u> into a drinking utensil.

2. Make <u>nip</u> into something sharp.

3. Make <u>cheap</u> into a fruit.

4. Make <u>tar</u> into a small animal.

5. Make <u>loop</u> into a small pond.

6. Make <u>net</u> into a number.

UNIT 2

Reading: Finding details

Dad took me for a walk along the docks. There were many ships tied up at the wharves. Two sailors were balanced on a plank over the side of one. They were painting the ship black. In another, men were unloading drums of oil. There was a smell of fish as we came upon a trawler. Sailors were cleaning the deck with a hose and brushes. They told us that they had just unloaded a catch of salmon.

In your notebook, complete each sentence by using a word from the box.

```
white    fish    farmers    black    oil    salmon    sailors
```

1. One ship was painted _____.

2. The trawler smelled of _____.

3. People who work on a ship are called _____.

4. The fish that was unloaded was _____.

Word Knowledge: More about sailors and ships

Match each word from the box to its meaning below. Write each word with its meaning in your notebook.

```
seafarer    harbour    bunk    yacht    oar    funnel
    fleet    ferry    captain    tug    stern    rudder
```

1. another name for port

2. Smoke comes from it.

3. another name for sailor

4. a ship's commander

5. It pulls other ships.

6. used for steering

7. sailor's bed

8. It carries people and cars.

9. many ships

10. a large, luxurious boat

11. back of a ship

12. used for rowing

Sentences: Questions

A sentence that asks a question begins with a capital letter and ends with a question mark. Remember that a sentence must make sense by itself. Write the sentences that are questions. Put in the question mark.

1. Can horses gallop
2. What is her name
3. He is very old
4. Do you like tea
5. Tom lives here
6. When I leave school
7. How many do you have
8. Why are you here
9. After the party
10. Where is the pen
11. Over the hill
12. She came yesterday

Usage: Using only the words we need

When speaking or writing sentences, we should use only the words we need. Write these sentences leaving out a word that is not needed.

1. I have got a puppy at home.
2. That there pencil is mine.
3. This man he spoke to me.
4. These here apples belong to me.
5. That girl she took my sweater.
6. We have got a motor boat.

Grammar: Verbs

Verbs are very important words. Every sentence must have a verb. Most verbs tell us about an action, so we often call them **doing words**.

A cook **bakes** cakes.   Fish **swim** in lakes.

Write the sentences using a suitable verb from the box in each space.

growl   eating   paint   flew   rides   play

1. The bird ____ away.
2. I like ____ ice cream.
3. Some dogs ____.
4. My sister ____ a pony.
5. Children ____ with toys.
6. We ____ pictures.

Draw a circle around the verb in each sentence.

Dictionary Skills: The alphabet

a b c d e f g h i j k l m n o p q r s t u v w x y z

Write the letter that comes after each of the following.

1. m
2. o
3. h
4. g
5. b
6. i
7. w
8. q
9. k
10. n
11. t
12. v

Written Expression: Finishing a story

Copy the first two sentences then finish the story yourself. Choose a title for your story.

One early morning I found a baby rabbit on our doorstep. Gently I picked up the little creature. Taking ____

Word Families: 'Uff' as in 'puff'

The words in the box belong to the same family of sounds.

> cuff   puff   bluff   snuff   scruff

Write new words of the same family from the clues.

1. soft downy bits

2. what a thing is made of

3. harsh in voice

4. walk without lifting the feet

Add a Letter

Make new words by adding the letters **d, s** or **t** to the beginning of each word. Use each of these letters twice.

1. rag   **2.** rod   **3.** pan   **4.** nip   **5.** rug   **6.** win

Just For Fun: Compound words

Compound words are two words that run together to form one word; for example, haystack. Use the letters below each diagram, as well as those in the squares, to make a compound word. The first part of the word reads across and the second part reads down. Copy the diagrams and letters into your notebooks. When you have worked out each puzzle, write the compound word.

1.

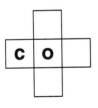

w b y

2.

g u e

3.

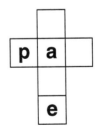

n k c

Reading: What kind of person?

On Sunday it was lovely and sunny. The twins, Pauline and Pamela, were having breakfast. Mother suggested that the girls should help her do some weeding in the garden.

"Yes, Mom, I'll help you. There is such a lot of work to be done," said Pauline.

"Oh, forget the weeds!" said Pam in a tired voice. "I'll lie in the sun and finish that book I was reading."

"Why Pam," said Mother, "you made the same excuse last night when it was time to wash the dishes."

"Yes, and what about last Sunday? Dad asked us to help clean the car. You were too busy looking after that baby bird that had fallen out of its nest," added Pauline.

Write the sentences that are true.

1. Pauline is not helpful at home.
2. Pauline is kind to animals.
3. Pam is helpful at home.
4. Pam is kind to animals.

Word Knowledge: Synonyms

Words that mean the same or nearly the same are synonyms. Choose words from the box that mean the same as the words below. Write them in your notebook.

halt	wet	little	start	price	bump
aged	wicked	leap	rob	glad	brag

1. knock	4. happy	7. evil	10. jump
2. stop	5. begin	8. cost	11. old
3. steal	6. damp	9. boast	12. small

Sentences: Best endings

Choose the best ending to finish these sentences. Write the whole sentence. Don't forget that each sentence must make sense.

1. The house _____.
   [a red roof, how many, is very old]

2. My uncle _____.
   [brown curly hair, in the new shop, drives a bus]

3. Cows _____.
   [in the paddocks, give us milk, on the farm]

4. Alice Kwan _____.
   [lives in Victoria, two cats at home, in the same class]

5. Milk is sold in _____.
   [a new van, brings the milk, bottles and cartons]

6. The beach _____.
   [is down the road, full of people, on the other side]

Punctuation: Capitals, periods and question marks

Rewrite these sentences putting in the punctuation marks.

1. how old is harry

2. do hens have teeth

3. the old woman is ill

4. she bought a new car

5. he lives by the creek

6. why were you late

Grammar: Common nouns and verbs

Every sentence must have a verb. A verb and a common noun will make a very short sentence. Use one word from the list of common nouns and one word from the list of verbs to make a sensible sentence. For example: Dogs bark. Make a sentence for each of the nouns and verbs.

common nouns			verbs		
dogs	pigs	jets	bark	fly	cut
clocks	knives	bells	tick	grunt	ring

Dictionary Skills: The alphabet

a b c d e f g h i j k l m n o p q r s t u v w x y z

Write the letter that comes before each of the following.

1. h	3. l	5. y	7. c	9. j	6. p
2. u	4. i	6. s	8. f	10. w	12. q

Written Expression: Sentences in order

Write each group of three sentences in the correct order. Then write three sentences of your own that are not in order. Ask a friend to write them in order.

1. Mom put candles on it. Everyone had a piece. Mom bought a cake.

2. He then posted it. Jim wrote a letter. He bought a stamp.

3. The alarm clock rang. I was late for school. I went back to sleep.

Word Families: 'Ack' as in 'pack'

The words in the box belong to the same family of sounds.

> back   pack   rack   stack   track

Write new words of the same family from the clues.

1. bag made of cloth   **3.** a colour

2. to slap   **4.** light meal

Add a Letter

Make new words by adding the letter **h** to the words below.

1. case   **2.** air   **3.** sock   **4.** tin   **5.** ten   **6.** tongs

Just For Fun: Homonyms

Can you solve the puzzle? Each pair of words sound the same but are spelled differently.

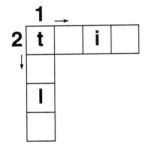

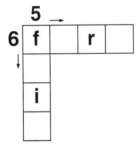

1. A dog has one.   **3.** female cleaner   **5.** payment for a

2. a story   **4.** We ____ a sand   train ride

castle.   **6.** not dark

More Fun

Copy each word. Next to it write any smaller words you see in the whole word.

1. plain   **2.** struck   **3.** soil   **4.** crowd   **5.** growl   **6.** repent

UNIT 4

Reading: The odd sound

Write each row of words. Three words in each row have the same vowel sound. Circle the word that does not belong.

1. fat catch hate wag

2. find file ring grind

3. five mind died film

4. plump drum spun mule

5. brag slam snag grade

6. print kite fine tried

7. boat cost told bowl

8. tube thud glum jump

Word Knowledge: Antonyms

Words that mean the opposite are antonyms. Choose words from the box that are opposite to the words below. Write them in your notebook.

dirty   easy   high   hilly   lose   whole
outside   found   cold   bright   close   few

1. many   **3.** dull   **5.** hot   **7.** difficult   **9.** flat   **11.** lost

2. inside   **4.** open   **6.** clean   **8.** find   **10.** part   **12.** low

Sentences: Matching endings

Complete each sentence by choosing a sensible ending from the box. Write them in your notebook.

1. The two pigs _____.

2. Her father's _____.

3. The pop star _____.

4. Several birds _____.

5. At the beach _____.

played the guitar
we swim in a safe area
were pecking corn
tie is green and yellow
squealed with fright

Usage: To, two and too

These three words can be confusing. Notice how they are used.

To is part of an action. He went **to** town.

Too means also. Will he come, **too?**

Too also gives strength to the following word. It is **too** hot to play.

Two is the number. I have **two** skateboards.

Write the sentences below using **to, too** or **two** to complete them.

1. We all have _____ feet.

2. It is _____ cold _____ swim.

3. He is _____ young _____ read the book.

4. Are you going _____ school?

5. May I have a plum _____?

6. The _____ boys were _____ tired _____ carry the logs.

Grammar: Proper nouns

Proper nouns are words used to name particular people, places and things. They always begin with a capital letter.

Megan lives in **Newcastle.**   I met **Mr. Singh** on **Sunday.**

Match the proper nouns from the box to the words below. Write them in your notebook.

```
Mario    July    Vancouver    Friday    Italy    Susan
```

1. a city

2. a month

3. a girl

4. a boy

5. a day

6. a country

Dictionary Skills: The alphabet

a b c d e f g h i j k l m n o p q r s t u v w x y z

Write the letter that comes before each of the following.

1. m

2. k

3. v

4. d

5. o

6. n

7. b

8. t

9. r

10. e

11. x

12. g

Written Expression: Rhyming words

Dimitri wrote a silly story. Instead of using the right words he used five others that rhymed. Read the story below then rewrite it to make it sensible using words that rhyme with his.

> One cold winter day I put on my boat and went for a talk along the street. At the corner shop I fought some chocolate. On the way home I met a fan with a dog on a drain.

Now that you have finished, write a silly story of your own using five wrong words that rhyme with the right ones. Ask another person to correct your story.

Word Families: 'Ell' as in 'bell'

The words in the box belong to the same family of sounds.

> dell   sell   fell   spell

Write new words of the same family from the clues.

1. not ill   **2.** shout loudly   **3.** grow larger   **4.** It rings.

Add a Letter

Make new words by adding the letter **r** to the words below.

1. ton   **2.** dip   **3.** tea   **4.** ice   **5.** tip   **6.** bush

Just For Fun: Word pyramids

Copy the pyramids. Fill in the squares.

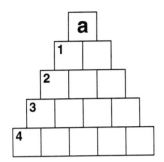

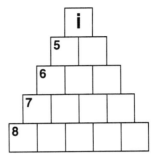

1. He is ____ home.

2. I ____ my dog.

3. We went ____ your house.

4. Stick the paper with ____.

5. Give ____ to me.

6. ____ on the chair.

7. to make a long narrow cut

8. to break into parts

More Fun

Find the six colours that are hidden in the square. Write them in your notebook. Words run across and down.

A	D	H	J	L	N	P	R
S	Y	E	L	L	O	W	B
I	V	W	O	U	B	F	L
X	P	U	R	P	L	E	A
C	Q	G	A	A	U	T	C
Y	O	B	N	Z	E	B	K
D	E	F	G	R	E	E	N
H	F	C	E	G	E	K	M

UNIT 5

Reading: Categories of words

Read each group of words. Choose a word from the box that names the category. Write each group of words and its category into your notebook.

> insects   vegetables   animals   trees   clothes
> metals   furniture   cities

1. skirt dress blouse coat

2. cow sheep lamb goat

3. Toronto Montreal Winnipeg Moncton

4. table chair bed dresser

5. wasp fly bee flea

6. tin lead silver gold

7. cabbage potato carrot spinach

8. oak elm pine willow

Word Knowledge: Occupations

Read the words in the box. Choose words from the box that match the meanings below. Write each word with its meaning in your notebook.

> miner   firefighter   pilot   hairdresser
> carpenter   dentist   farmer   teller
> baker   nurse   teacher   butcher

1. A _____ flies airplanes.

2. A _____ works in a hospital.

3. A _____ works in a school.

4. A _____ bakes bread.

5. A _____ cares for teeth.

6. A _____ works in a bank.

7. A _____ cuts hair.

8. A _____ works underground.

9. A _____ sells meat.

10. A _____ works with wood.

11. A _____ fights fires.

12. A _____ grows crops.

Sentences: Joining with 'and'

The joining word **and** can be used to join the names of two people doing the same thing.

> Judith played on the swings. I played on the swings.
> Judith **and** I played on the swings.

Join each pair of sentences with **and**.

1. Mario went to the football game. Charles went to the football game.
2. My brother swam in the pool. I swam in the pool.
3. Ali played in the tennis match. Lorraine played in the tennis match.
4. Maria went skiing. Jose went skiing.

Punctuation: Capitals, periods and question marks

Rewrite each sentence and put in the correct punctuation.

1. may i go to the playground
2. the endeavour sailed the pacific ocean
3. robert goes to elmdale public school
4. we shop at smith brothers
5. i had fun on new year's day
6. tim's birthday is in january

Grammar: More proper nouns

Proper nouns can consist of two or more words naming particular people, places and things.

> Oil is found in **Alberta**.   She lives in **George Street**.

Match the proper nouns from the box to the words below. Write them in your notebook.

```
High Street    Canada Day    Mount Everest    Red River
```

1. a day   **2.** a mountain   **3.** a river   **4.** a street

19

Dictionary Skills: Alphabetical Order

Put each group of letters into alphabetical order.

1. u r v z

2. r m o a

3. j k d m

4. p n u x

5. o r x t

6. g w l n

7. g u l p

8. q z o i

9. i s c j

10. m x y j

11. c b f m

12. t r s u

Written Expression: Rhyming lines

Write the pairs of lines. Fill in the blanks with a word that rhymes with the last one in the line above.

1. The big fat pig

   Danced a little _____.

2. Mrs. Tam's hen

   Lived in a _____.

Now make up rhymes to go with these lines.

3. The old black trunk

4. When I go to camp

5. Be careful when you skip

6. Dad dropped the cake

Word Families: 'Ink' as in 'wink'

The words in the box belong to the same family of sounds.

> ink   kink   link   wink   brink

Write new words of the same family from the clues.

1. a colour   **2.** go down   **3.** take in liquid   **4.** a bad smell

Just For Fun: Anagrams

Rearrange the underlined words to make new words.

1. Make <u>eat</u> into a drink.

2. Make <u>tip</u> into a hole.

3. Make <u>reap</u> into a fruit.

4. Make <u>low</u> into a bird.

5. Make <u>arm</u> into an animal.

6. Make <u>leak</u> into a body of water.

Reading: One fact too many

Read the problems carefully. In each one you will find a sentence that is unnecessary for finding the answer. Write each unnecessary sentence in your notebook.

1. Dad grew twelve pumpkins in the garden. He also had six tomato plants. All the pumpkins except two were used by the family. How many pumpkins did the family have altogether?

2. I live exactly three kilometres from school. Each day I pay 80 cents for a return bus ticket. Last week I only attended school on three days. How much did I spend that week on bus fare?

Word Knowledge: Verbs that are sounds

Read the words in the box. Use these words to make short sentences with the nouns below. Write each complete sentence in your notebook.

```
        crow    squeak   cluck    bark    chirp
        roar    jangle   slam     neigh   quack
                    buzz     honk
```

1. Horses ____.
2. Lions ____.
3. Roosters ____.
4. Sparrows ____.

5. Ducks ____.
6. Bees ____.
7. Doors ____.
8. Dogs ____.

9. Hens ____.
10. Mice ____.
11. Chains ____.
12. Horns ____.

Sentences: Joining two ideas with 'and'

When the same person does two things, we may use **and** to join the two ideas into one sentence.

The cat opened its eyes. It yawned.
The cat opened its eyes **and** yawned.

Join each pair of sentences with the word 'and.'

1. Walter picked up his pen. He started writing.

2. The cat saw the mouse. She sprang at it.

3. The driver saw the truck. He swerved to avoid a collision.

4. We all lay on the beach. We enjoyed the warm sun.

Usage: 'Hear' and 'here'

Hear means to hear with your ears.   I **hear** the dog barking.
Here means in this place.   The ball is over **here**.

Write each sentence and use **hear** or **here** in the spaces.

1. A rabbit can _____ well with its ears.

2. The birds do not come _____ any more.

3. I am _____ to _____ the music.

4. "Come _____ at once!" she called.

5. I can't _____ you because of the noise in _____.

6. Can you come _____?

Grammar: More verbs and nouns

Complete each sentence by choosing a verb from the box. Write the whole sentence.

```
gallops   glides   hops   prowls   swims   crawls
```

1. A kangaroo _____.   **3.** A caterpillar _____.   **5.** A snake _____.

2. A horse _____.   **4.** A fish _____.   **6.** A lion _____.

Dictionary Skills: Alphabetical order

Put each group of letters into alphabetical order.

1. b r c f   **5.** g e t w   **9.** w s p m

2. m l n q   **6.** l o s k   **10.** y t h x

3. g x m u   **7.** u t x z   **11.** y v u s

4. w u v z   **8.** e b c h   **12.** p s t v

Written Expression: Practising sentences

Make up a sentence that includes all three words. Then write a second sentence that follows on from the first one. Write twelve sentences altogether. Use describing words.

1. have   elephants   trunks

2. bone   dog   gave

3. took   beach   rod

4. zoo   monkey   cage

5. ball   game   soccer

6. tree   plane   crashed

Word Families: 'Ash' as in 'crash'

The words in the box belong to the same family of sounds.

> lash   mash   bash   rash   smash

Write new words of the same family from the clues.

1. money   **2.** run quickly   **3.** cut   **4.** Cars do this.

Add a Letter

Make new words by adding the letter **r** to the words below.

1. bake   **2.** band   **3.** pint   **4.** hose   **5.** beak   **6.** dead

Just For Fun: Compound words

Complete the compound words. Remember that the first part of the compound word reads across. The second part reads down. Copy the diagrams and letters. When you have worked out each word write it in full.

1.

2.

3.

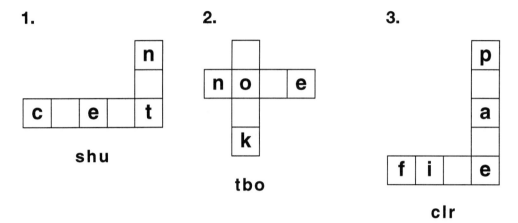

More Fun

Find the six cities that are hidden in the square. Write them in your notebook. Cities run across and down.

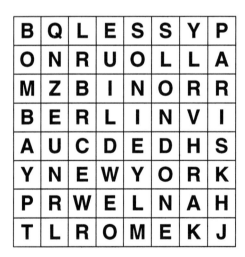

B	Q	L	E	S	S	Y	P
O	N	R	U	O	L	L	A
M	Z	B	I	N	O	R	R
B	E	R	L	I	N	V	I
A	U	C	D	E	D	H	S
Y	N	E	W	Y	O	R	K
P	R	W	E	L	N	A	H
T	L	R	O	M	E	K	J

Reading: The main idea

Read the paragraph then the list below. Choose a sentence from the list that describes the main idea of the paragraph.

> Of all Anna's birthday presents her model plane pleased her most. She read all the instructions and then carefully put the pieces together. When the plane was finished she painted it brown and green. How proud she was to have built it all by herself.

1. Anna is always given a model for her birthday.
2. Anna painted her plane.
3. Anna enjoyed building her plane.
4. Anna was a clever girl.

Word Knowledge: Containers

Each object goes into a container. Match the containers from the box to their objects below. Write them in your notebook.

> dam   bin   album   vase   pot
> purse   closet   stable   silo
> briefcase   garage   envelope

1. letter	4. tea	7. horse	10. money
2. car	5. clothes	8. grain	11. papers
3. flowers	6. photographs	9. water	12. garbage

Sentences: Recognizing one

Are these sentences? Read the groups of words. Write each complete sentence.

1. Because she was late
2. The bus was late
3. Cows give milk
4. Parrots can talk
5. Sugar tastes sweet

6. The cat ran away
7. By the fence
8. When I lived in Halifax
9. Over the tall fence

Punctuation: Writing the date

When we write the date we use a capital letter for the month. We use numerals for the number. We use a comma before the year.

May 17, 1994

Write the following dates:

1. the last day next year
2. the date next Christmas Day
3. next Sunday's date

4. the first day next year
5. the date you were born
6. today's date

Grammar: Forms of the verb 'to be'

Most verbs describe an action. One verb that does not really describe an action is the verb **to be**. It has different forms.

I **am** at home.   She **is** over there.   They **are** in the water.

Write each sentence using the above forms of the verb to be.

1. Jim _____ in the pool.
2. I _____ on the floor.
3. He _____ in the room.

4. We _____ very cold.
5. You _____ not well.
6. They _____ by the creek.

Dictionary Skills: Alphabetical order

Put each group of letters into alphabetical order.

1. d j p m

2. o r e z

3. p m h k

4. l j n m

5. z x y w

6. h k f n

7. l k o s

8. o l r v

9. o w m s

10. t x q v

11. c b d f

12. z w s p

Written Expression: A mixed-up story

Read this story. Rewrite it by rearranging some words to make it sensible. Use only the words given to you.

> On hot days Ahmed sits by the fire. He likes to go swimming when the weather is cold. Ahmed plays with his pet tigers. Reading is one of his hobbies. He likes books about cats.

Now that you have finished, write your own mixed-up story. Ask a friend to write it correctly.

Word Families: 'Ing' as in 'sing'

The words in the box belong to the same family of sounds.

```
            sing    wing    cling    fling
```

Write new words of the same family from the clues.

1. queen's husband

2. Bees do this.

3. worn on the finger

4. used for tying things

Add a Letter

Make new words by adding the letter **l** to these words.

1. hoe   **2.** gum   **3.** came   **4.** fat   **5.** pant   **6.** bed

Just For Fun: Homonyms

Copy and complete the puzzle. Each pair of words sound the same but are spelled differently.

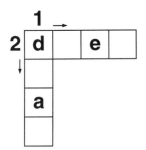

1 →
2 | d | | e | |

a

1. animal with horns
2. begins a letter:

   ____ Mom,

3 →
4 | b | | a | |

e

3. a vegetable
4. Have you

   ____ there?

5 →
6 | m | | i | |

l

5. letters and parcels
6. not female

More Fun

Find the four-letter animal that is hidden in each sentence. The first is done for you.

1. He lived long a**go at** the coast. (goat)
2. An emu leaves large footprints.
3. He put a post against the house.
4. Will you be around today?
5. The sun made Eric hot.
6. Put the cap on your head.
7. Grandma returns soon.

Reading: The odd sound

Write each row of words. Three words in each row have the same vowel sound. Circle the word that does not belong.

1. year   bear   jeer   ear
2. hear   dear   wear   near
3. round   toe   cow   down
4. great   bleat   steal   leap

5. gear   near   rear   pear
6. beak   break   streak   sneak
7. streak   tweak   steak   peak
8. hoe   our   out   now

Word Knowledge: Fruit and vegetables

Read the words in the box. Match the words from the box to their meanings below. Write them in your notebook.

> raisin   lettuce   tomato   banana   mustard   core
> bean   date   potato   lemon   melon   peel

1. red salad fruit
2. outer covering
3. grows on palms
4. long yellow fruit
5. plant with hot seeds
6. sweet dried grape

7. can be baked in tins
8. has sour juice
9. grows under the ground
10. leaf used in salads
11. largest fruit
12. inside of an apple

Sentences: Making statements and questions

Use each set of jumbled words twice. First make a sentence that is a statement. Then make a sentence that is a question. Don't forget periods and question marks.

1. at he is home
2. doctor the come has
3. gone they away have

Usage: 'A' or 'an'

We use **a** before nouns that begin with consonants. If a word begins with a vowel (a, e, i. o, u) we use **an**.

He ate **a** peach.   She ate **an** apple.

Write each of the words below. Put **a** or **an** in front of them.

1. monkey	**7.** rabbit	**13.** elephant
2. antelope	**8.** beaver	**14.** otter
3. asparagus	**9.** spinach	**15.** turnip
4. onion	**10.** eggplant	**16.** cabbage
5. Italian	**11.** Australian	**17.** painting
6. American	**12.** automobile	**18.** window

Grammar: Verbs 'to have' and 'to do'

Other verbs that do not describe actions are **to have** and **to do**.

I **have** a pet bird.   Jason **does** the washing.

Write each sentence using one of the words in brackets.

1. Sally (has have) a bucket of sand.

2. We (has have) two ducks at home.

3. They (has have) a new car.

4. My sister (do does) the coaching.

5. Small ants (do does) all the work.

6. We (do does) the dishes.

Dictionary Skills: Alphabetical order

Put each group of words into alphabetical order.

1. meal rush else less	**5.** drop gain love comb
2. iron chase grey pass	**6.** money other smash porch
3. knot tiny house maid	**7.** noon lion once poor
4. fork less earth only	**8.** taste uncle where sport

Written Expression: You are Tom Thumb

Imagine that you are Tom Thumb. You are only four centimetres tall. Tell about an adventure that you had.

Word Families: 'Ick' as in 'pick'

The words in the box belong to the same family of sounds.

> kick   lick   pick   tick   trick

Write new words of the same family from the clues.

1. not well

2. used to build houses

3. used in a lamp

4. a twig

Add a Letter

Make new words by adding the letter **l** to these words.

1. sat   **2.** eaves   **3.** sit   **4.** bet   **5.** fog   **6.** met

Just For Fun: Word pyramids

Copy the pyramids. Add one more letter each time.

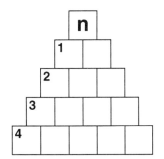

1. not yes

2. less than two

3. You smell with it.

4. The sun _____.

5. I _____ working.

6. a rug

7. not wild

8. water gas

Reading: Categories of words

Read each group of words. Choose a word from the box that names the category. Write each group of words and its category in your notebook.

> names   birds   insects   countries
> tools   days   fish   fruits

1. hammer chisel pliers saw

2. salmon trout tuna cod

3. Jill Indira Maria Kim

4. apple grape plum peach

5. moth butterfly cricket ant

6. duck goose hen turkey

7. Canada Australia China India

8. Wednesday Monday Sunday Thursday

Word Knowledge: Words about the weather

Read the words in the box. Choose words from the box that match the meanings below. Write each word with is meaning in your notebook.

> rain   lightning   cyclone   smog   fog   gale
> drizzle   blizzard   frost   thunder   breeze   hail

1. frozen dew

2. frozen rain

3. violent snowstorm

4. water from clouds

5. thick mist

6. strong wind

7. very violent windstorm

8. electricity in the sky

9. smoke and fog

10. light rain

11. noise in the sky

12. light wind

Sentences: Joining words with 'but'

Two sentences that would not usually go together may be joined by **but**. The second verb can be left out.

The day was sunny. It was cold.
The day was sunny **but** cold.

Make one sentence from each pair. Leave out the second verb.

1. The bed is old. It is comfortable.

2. The oranges were small. They were juicy.

3. The girl was ill. She was cheerful.

4. The string was thin. It was strong.

Punctuation: Names of months and seasons

The names of the months begin with capital letters. The names of the seasons do not.

Months

January   February   March   April   May   June   July
August   September   October   November   December

Seasons

spring   summer   autumn   winter

Write each sentence by using the correct months in the spaces.

1. The months of spring are ____, ____ and ____.

2. The months of summer are ____, ____ and ____.

3. The months of autumn are ____, ____ and ____.

4. The months of winter are ____, ____ and ____.

Grammar: Plural nouns—adding 's'

Plural means 'more than one.' Most words add **s** to form the plural

one rabbit   two rabbits

Copy each noun but make it plural.

1. lamb   **3.** river   **5.** skin   **7.** spade

2. pear   **4.** pump   **6.** paper   **8.** house

Dictionary Skills: Alphabetical order

Put each group of words into alphabetical order.

1. motor glove fight carry
2. warm taxi you very
3. meal life past rest
4. close early dance heavy
5. knee hour lead mark
6. engine behind market police
7. hungry invite finish silver
8. test wait soap yacht

Written Expression: New nursery rhymes

Finish this made-up nursery rhyme by adding three more lines. Then make up a new one of your own.

> Little Jack Platt
> Sat on a mat,
> Eating a juicy pear,

Word Families: 'Ang' as in 'rang'

The words in the box belong to the same family of sounds.

gang   hang   slang   clang   sprang

Write new words of the same family from the clues.

1. loud noise
2. snake's tooth
3. The bell _____.
4. We _____ songs.

Just For Fun: Anagrams

Rearrange the letters of each underlined word to make new words.

1. Make nib into a container.
2. Make tub into a joining word.
3. Make was into a tool.
4. Make slap into friends.
5. Make eat into a drink.
6. Make tool into a word meaning stolen goods.

Reading: Finding facts

There are many kinds of hummingbirds. Some grow to fifteen centimetres long. Others are as small as two centimetres—no longer than a bee. These birds get their names from the humming sound made by their wings.

A hummingbird can stay in one spot in the air. This is called hovering. By flapping its wings very fast, it can remain as if hung on a string. The bird hovers over a flower, then pokes its beak inside. Nectar is sucked out with the tongue, which is shaped like a tube.

Write two sentences that are true.

1. Hummingbirds use their beaks for flying.

2. To fly in one spot is to hover.

3. A hummingbird feeds on nectar.

4. Many hummingbirds are smaller than one centimetre.

Word Knowledge: More about birds

Read the words in the box. Match the words from the box to their meanings below. Write each word with its meaning into your notebook.

| rooster turkey penguin kookaburra |
| eagle crow beak hatch nest |

1. It lives in cold lands.

2. a male chicken

3. a bird that hunts

4. to come out of an egg

5. a bird's home

6. a bird's mouth

7. an Australian bird that laughs

8. a black bird

9. largest bird we eat

Sentences: Joining with 'and' or 'but'

Words that join sentences are called conjunctions. Join these sentences by using **and** or **but**.

1. The dog sniffed the bone. He would not eat it.
2. We dug holes in the sand. We built castles.
3. The baby bumped her head. She did not cry.
4. The rabbit saw the dog. It scampered to its burrow.
5. I went to town. I bought some cheese.
6. Terry tried to catch the ball. He missed it.

Usage: 'Of' and 'off'

I like a glass **of** milk.   Jim took his coat **off** the peg.

Write each sentence using **of** or **off** in the blank spaces.

1. We each drank a bottle _____ lemonade at the party.
2. The cat leaped _____ the wall into the garden.
3. A truck carrying a load _____ steel ran _____ the road.
4. All _____ them ran _____ along the beach.
5. Part _____ the statue was broken _____.
6. Hans set _____ a rocket from the top _____ the hill.

Grammar: Plural nouns ending in 'ch'

Nouns that end in **ch** form their plural by adding **es**.

one ditch   two ditches

Write the plural forms of these nouns.

1. bunch   2. pitch   3. coach   4. watch

36

Dictionary Skills: Alphabetical order

Put each group of words into alphabetical order.

1. tooth   uncle   sugar   voice

2. quiet   paste   sheet   light

3. valley   daisies   strange   through

4. rather   throat   pencil   smooth

5. divide   cheese   either   finger

6. caught   ladder   branch   hoping

7. meal   once   rate   salt

8. ground   lesson   people   forest

Written Expression: Retelling a story

Tell the story of *The Three Bears* in your own words but make up a different ending.

Just For Fun: Compound words

Copy and complete the puzzles.

1.

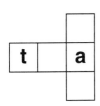

ebg

2.

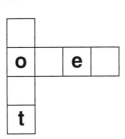

acrv

3.

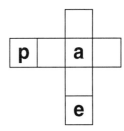

lmty

More Fun

Use **ea, oa, ee**, three times each to complete the words. Write them in your notebook.

1. c ____ t

2. h ____ t

3. p ____ p

4. f ____ m

5. h ____ p

6. f ____ l

7. d ____ p

8. g ____ l

9. n ____ r

Reading: Drawing conclusions

After reading a paragraph you can decide things about the contents. This is called drawing conclusions. Read this passage, then choose the two correct conclusions from the six below. Write them in your notebook.

> Fruits are an important food. They are full of acids, salts and vitamins that help us keep a balanced diet. Even the water and roughage are good for us. Dentists advise us to eat fresh fruit instead of chocolate and candy. By doing this we are less likely to get holes in our teeth.

1. We should sometimes eat fruit.
2. We should think about fruit.
3. We should eat plenty of fruit.
4. Fruit is especially good for dentists.
5. By eating fruit we may avoid tooth decay.
6. Dentists tell us to eat chocolates and candy.

Word Knowledge: Synonyms

Choose words from the box that mean the same as each word below. Write them in your notebook.

```
   own    package    scare    permit    round    tumble
      heat    whip    talk    snatch    peek    rogue
```

1. frighten
2. possess
3. warmth
4. beat
5. allow
6. fall
7. circular
8. peep
9. parcel
10. grab
11. speak
12. rascal

Sentences: Fixing mistakes

The printer made some mistakes. Parts of one sentence belong to another. Rearrange them to make sense.

1. The horse filled her tooth.
2. The boy crowed each morning.
3. Boats fly in the air.
4. The dentist has four legs.
5. Planes sail on the sea.
6. The rooster plays with toys.

Punctuation: Review

Rewrite each sentence putting in all the punctuation marks and capital letters.

1. jim has a dog named fido
2. are you coming on tuesday
3. he was born april 20, 1982
4. in australia july is a winter month
5. last week i read black beauty
6. does uncle harry come from Sydney

Grammar: Adjectives

Adjectives are words that tell us more about or describe nouns. They tell what kind, or which, what colour or how many.

She has a **new** bicycle.   He wore a **blue** shirt.
I ate **two** buns.

In your notebook, write each sentence by using an adjective from the box to fill each space.

```
cruel    sharp    rich    five
```

1. He cut himself on the _____ knife.
2. We have _____ fingers on each hand.
3. The _____ man gave money to charity.
4. The _____ boy kicked the dog.

Dictionary Skills: Pairs of letters in alphabetical order

Write the pairs of letters in alphabetical order for each group.

1. so sa su se
2. fu fl fi fr
3. sw sd sp sl
4. wh fl tr sm
5. th sh wh wr

6. dr gr sl pl
7. ri re ro ru
8. hi he ho hu
9. sl gl qu sk
10. qu ch cu sc

Written Expression: Riddles

Can you guess the objects? The first begins with **s** and the second with **h**. Then write three riddles of your own and give them to someone else in the class to solve.

1. I am cold and wet.
   I am full of bubbles.
   You drink me.

2. I taste sweet.
   I am made from nectar.
   Bees make me.

Word Families: 'Ock' as in 'clock'

The words in the box belong to the same family of sounds.

> lock   stock   block   frock

Write new words of the same family from the clues.

1. a group of sheep

2. It tells the time.

3. worn on the foot

4. stone

Add a Letter

Make new words by adding the letter **p** to these words.

1. ram   **2.** sin   **3.** hum   **4.** sit   **5.** sum   **6.** act

Just For Fun: Homonyms

Copy and complete the puzzles. Each pair of words sound the same but are spelled differently.

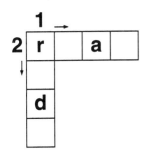 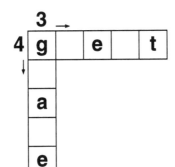 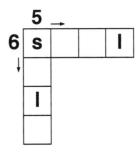

1. A bus runs on it.

2. She _____ a horse.

3. huge

4. part of a fireplace

5. A boat may have one.

6. He bought it on _____ .

More Fun

Copy each word. Next to it write any smaller words you see in the whole word.

1. glove   **3.** crust   **5.** polite

2. train   **4.** towel   **6.** pretend

UNIT 12

Reading: The odd sound

Write each row of words. Three words in each row have the same vowel sound. Circle the word that does not belong.

1. sand   salt   sack   ramp

2. hall   fall   calf   tall

3. sworn   thorn   storm   worm

4. worth   fourth   north   torch

5. half   swat   swab   wash

6. word   cord   born   torn

7. stork   work   sort   port

8. ball   gallon   gallop   shallow

Word Knowledge: Antonyms

Choose words from the box that are opposite in meaning to the words below. Write each word and its opposite in your notebook.

> under   empty   hard   something   straight
> cloudy   smooth   less   before   outer
> backwards   apart

1. nothing
2. rough
3. sunny

4. soft
5. forward
6. more

7. full
8. after
9. crooked

10. over
11. together
12. inner

Sentences: Prepositions; adjectival phrases

Prepositions are words that are placed before a noun. Here are some prepositions that are often used:

> in   came   under   over   of
>
> on   with   off   for   into   after

Choose a preposition from the box to complete each sentence.

1. Franco and Mary went skateboarding _____ the park.
2. Franco fell _____ the board.
3. Mary came _____ to help him.
4. Franco had cuts _____ his legs.
5. Franco walked home _____ Mary.
6. Franco put his skateboard _____ his bed.

A **phrase** is a group of words beginning with a preposition. A phrase is not a sentence by itself. It can describe a noun or a verb.

> The boat **with red sails** hit the rock.

Here the phrase **with red sails** acts as an adjective as it describes the boat.

In your notebook, complete each sentence by adding a **phrase** from the box to each space. Underline your phrases when you have finished. Draw a circle around the noun each one describes.

> about pirates   in the vase   with four engines
>
> from the butcher's   in the river   on the wall

7. The jet _____ landed.
8. The meat _____ was tough.
9. The water _____ was muddy.
10. I like reading books _____.
11. The flowers _____ were pretty.
12. The picture _____ is valuable.

43

Usage: 'Their' and 'there'

Their means belonging to them.

There means in that place. **There** can be used at the beginning of a sentence before a verb.

The man spoke to **their** mother.   The station is over **there**.

There are mice in the cupboard.

Write each sentence putting **their** or **there** in the spaces.

1. A fox is hiding over _____.

2. _____ are clouds in the sky.

3. The girls enjoyed _____ outing.

4. Let's go over _____ and see _____ new car.

5. _____ is a goat over _____ in _____ field.

Grammar: Adjectives that are colours

In your notebook, complete each sentence using an adjective from the box in the spaces.

> yellow   green   red   white   blue   grey

1. Your blood is _____.

2. A banana skin is _____.

3. Rainy skies are _____.

4. Cars go when lights are _____.

5. The sheet was as _____ as snow.

6. He wore a navy _____ coat.

Dictionary Skills: Pairs of letters in alphabetical order

Write the pair of letters in alphabetical order for each group.

1. fo fl fe fr   **4.** do du di de   **7.** sk sp sw st

2. qu sp wh th   **5.** ji ju jo ja   **8.** gl gu go gr

3. gi ge gu go   **6.** we wr wh wo   **9.** ko ku ki ke

Written Expression: A story from a picture

Study the picture. Write a story about it.

Word Families: 'ill' as in 'drill'

The words in the box belong to the same family of sounds.

swill   drill   trill   frill   quill

Write new words of the same family from the clues.

1. to broil   **2.** let water fall   **3.** not moving   **4.** not well

Just For Fun: Word pyramids

Copy the pyramids. Fill in the squares.

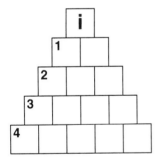

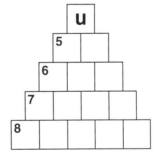

1. not out

2. It has a point.

3. kind of wood

4. backbone

5. we

6. It carries people.

7. plant

8. to sweep

Reading: Moods we feel

Read the passage carefully.

> One day at school we were asked to talk about pets. Julie told the class about her parrot called Percy. She said that Percy would knock his beak on the table whenever she said "Knock on wood, Percy."
>
>   Of course a number of us went to Julie's house to see this amazing parrot. Julie repeated the words over and over but the silly bird just stood moving its head from side to side.

Did Julie feel happy, silly or proud? Write one or two sentences telling how Julie felt and why she felt like that.

Word Knowledge: Clothes

Read the words in the box. Match each word from the box to its meaning below. Write the word and its meaning in your notebook.

```
belt    bootees    pyjamas    sleeper    tie
  gloves    sandal    jeans    scarf    vest
          pullover    blouse
```

1. an open shoe
2. worn around waist
3. woman's shirt
4. denim pants
5. men's neckwear
6. worn on baby's feet
7. baby's pyjamas
8. worn on the hands
9. worn around the neck
10. worn to bed
11. worn over shirt
12. sleeveless garment

Sentences: Questions

Match the questions in the box to the answers below. Write each question and answer in your notebook.

```
What do you want to be?    How old are you?
         What does your father do?
         What was the weather like?
What is your favourite colour?    Where is your dog?
```

1. I will be ten in November.

2. It rained all last week.

3. I like green best of all.

4. I hope to become a teacher.

5. He works in a store.

6. He is in his kennel.

Punctuation: Apostrophe of ownership

When something is owned by, or belongs to someone or something, the owner's name has an apostrophe to show this.

the cat's whisker   Mr. Dalton's house
Gwen's book

Write these phrases using the apostrophe in the correct place.

1. the players uniform

2. the elephants tusks

3. the pencils lead

4. the firefighters helmet

5. Jennys roller blades

6. Omans skateboard

Rewrite each phrase using the apostrophe.

1. the sails of a ship

2. the roar of a lion

3. the clubs of a golfer

4. the sister of Robert

5. the hat of the general

6. the feathers of a bird

Grammar: Adverbs

Adverbs are words that tell more about verbs. They add meaning to verbs. Adverbs tell **how, when** or **where** something is done.

Barry walked **quickly**. (how he walked)
Mavis is coming **late**. (when she will come)
The children ate **outside**. (where they ate)

Write each sentence by adding an adverb from the box.

happily	busily	slowly	greedily	loudly	angrily

1. Drums beat ____.   **3.** Children play ____.   **5.** Candles burn ____.

2. Cats spit ____.   **4.** Pigs eat ____.   **6.** Ants work ____.

Dictionary Skills: Pairs of letters in alphabetical order

1. tw te tr ta   **4.** re ro ri rh   **7.** sc sp sw st

2. fr ch gl th   **5.** sw cr gl pr   **8.** ph pl pr pi

3. mi mo mu me   **6.** ne ni nu na   **9.** la lo le li

Written Expression: A description

Pretend you have been writing to a pen pal in Africa. In one of your letters you mentioned a Canada goose. Your pen pal, who has never seen a Canada goose, has written for a full description of one. Write it for him or her.

Word Families: 'Ank' as in 'blank'

The words in the box belong to the same family of sounds.

> rank   yank   blank   drank   stank

Write new words of the same family from the clues.

1. building that holds money   **3.** It holds water.

2. piece of wood   **4.** playful trick

Just For Fun: Anagrams

Rearrange the letters of the underlined words to make new words.

1. Make pea into an animal.

2. Make dew into married.

3. Make slap into friends.

4. Make pal into drink like a dog.

5. Make gas into hang down.

6. Make deaf into 'become less bright.'

More Fun

Find the five animals that are hidden in the square. Write them in your notebook. Words run across and down.

R	A	M	O	O	S	E	E
S	U	K	L	Y	E	L	S
T	H	O	R	S	E	E	K
A	P	A	S	O	N	F	U
R	A	L	T	O	Y	O	N
F	L	A	N	Y	X	W	K

UNIT 14

Reading: The main idea

Read the paragraph. Choose a sentence from those below that describes the main idea of the paragraph.

Lions have great strength. Large males weigh as much as 200 kilograms but females are not as heavy. These animals live on the plains of Africa. They feed on antelopes and zebras. Lions strike with their powerful paws. One blow can break the hunted animal's neck.

1. Lions live on plains.

3. Lions feed on meat.

2. Lions are not friendly.

4. Lions are powerful hunters of animals.

Word Knowledge: Numbers

Write each sentence using the correct words from the box.

four	seven	five	two	twelve	eight
ten	one	nine	eleven	six	three

1. _____ is half a dozen.

2. _____ is one less than ten.

3. We have _____ toes on our feet.

4. There are _____ days in a week.

5. We have _____ fingers on each hand.

6. A dog has _____ legs.

7. We have _____ eyes.

8. One dozen is _____.

9. One more than seven is _____.

10. A baseball team has _____ players.

11. A cat has _____ tail.

12. A triangle has _____ sides.

Sentences: Questions that answer 'yes' or 'no'

Match the questions in the box to the answers below. Write each question and answer in your notebook.

Do cows eat meat?   Will your dog bite?
Are you going home?   Can you play the piano?
Are you older than Bob?   May I go to the movies?

1. Yes, if you have any money.
_____?

2. No, he is older than I am.
_____?

3. No, they mainly eat grass.
_____?

4. Yes, my mother wants me.
_____?

5. No, I have never learned.
_____?

6. Yes, if you tease him.
_____?

Usage: 'May' or 'can'

The word **may** asks permission. The word **can** means able to.

May I have a swim? (asking permission)
Can you swim? (Are you able?)

Use **may** or **can** in each space. Write the sentences in your notebook.

1. _____ we watch television please?

2. You _____ go inside if you _____ open the door.

3. How _____ I fix the puncture?

4. Miro _____ go if he cleans his room.

5. _____ your pet parrot talk?

6. Dianne _____ sing well.

Grammar: More adverbs

Complete each sentence by adding an adverb from the box. Write each sentence in your notebook.

down   fiercely   speedily   gracefully   soundly
neatly   politely   noisily   clumsily

1. We sleep ____.

2. We write ____.

3. Jets fly ____.

4. Ballet dancers dance ____.

5. Hail comes ____.

6. We should speak ____.

7. Children hammer ____.

8. Some people fumble ____.

9. Lions growl ____.

Dictionary Skills: Words beginning with the same letters

Write each line of words in dictionary order.

1. city   care   comb   club

2. woman   wheel   write   winter

3. blade   break   below   burst

4. small   shoes   snake   stand

5. hunt   high   heat   how

6. could   crack   cloud   chair

7. fresh   fence   fight   fruit

8. pear   pile   pump   pass

Written Expression: Writing a letter

Write a short letter to an uncle thanking him for a birthday present. Tell him some family news. Write your address and set up the letter like the one below.

18 Elm Street
Orillia, ON
M2P 2X8
June 18, 1994

Dear Uncle ____

    Thank _____

Lots of love,

Word Families: 'Ch' as in 'chest'

The words in the box belong to the same family of sounds. Write new words of the same family from the clues.

> chap   chum   chest   check   chink

1. talk   **2.** part of your face   **3.** fried potato   **4.** cut up

Just For Fun: Crosswords

Copy and complete the puzzles.

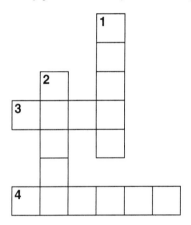
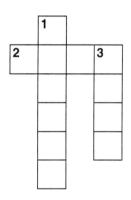

1. a birthday _____   **1.** bread and _____

2. Some people live in one.   **2.** a bird that quacks

3. like a yacht   **3.** I can fly a _____.

4. You mail it.

More Fun

Copy each word. Next to it write any smaller words you see in the whole word.

1. cloudy   **3.** danger   **5.** stool

2. cover   **4.** match   **6.** tender

UNIT 15

Reading: Information not needed

In the paragraph there is a sentence that does not belong. Decide which one it is and write it in your notebook.

> The dairy bar on the corner of George Street sells ice cream. Sometimes my brother Steven and I go there to buy a milkshake or an ice cream. Steven has a brand new bicycle. He always chooses a chocolate flavour.

Word Knowledge: Idioms

An idiom is a phrase or expression that cannot be understood from the ordinary meanings of the words in it. Write each sentence and use the correct idiom from the box.

> stone   horse   lip   cats   sack
> ghost   bird's   gold   roof   frog

1. Try to keep a stiff upper ____.
2. We had a ____ eye view from the plane.
3. I am so hungry I could eat a ____.
4. We haven't a ____ of a chance of winning.
5. It is raining ____ and dogs.
6. She has a heart of ____.
7. I'm so tired that I'll hit the ____.
8. The damaged canoe sank like a ____.
9. She had a ____ in her throat.
10. He will hit the ____ when he hears the news.

Sentences: Using phrases

A phrase is a group of words beginning with a preposition. A phrase is not a sentence by itself. It can tell us more about a noun or a verb.

Dad planted beans **along the fence**.

The phrase **along the fence** acts like an adverb and tells **where** he planted the beans.

In your notebook, complete each sentence by adding a phrase from the box.

off the rails	from the west	in the playground
in a cave	on the rocks	on its nose

1. The bear slept ____.

2. The boat became stuck ____.

3. We played ball ____.

4. A storm came ____.

5. The seal balanced a ball ____.

6. The train ran ____.

Underline each phrase then draw a circle around the verb in each sentence.

Punctuation: Writing your address

Below are three different addresses. Notice how they are written. Write your own address. Make sure that you have used capital letters if necessary.

17 Crown Road
Kingston, ON
M3R 2XY

34 York Street
Brandon, MN
R3K 5L5

28 Herrin Avenue
Truro, NS
B4N 8Y2

Grammar: Nouns, verbs and adverbs

Sort the words in the box into nouns, verbs and adverbs. Write them in your notebook.

```
walk    happily    bottles    pigs    clatter    turtles
grunt    slowly    noisily    climb    monkeys    easily
```

Write four sentences each containing a noun, verb and adverb. Use the words from the box. Remember to use a capital to begin a sentence.

Dictionary Skills: Words beginning with the same letters

Write each group of words in dictionary order.

1. tent time tall told

2. feel flew fair fork

3. branch button before baby

4. bridge beside bucket boat

5. chalk climb cover carry

6. thin true team tale

7. seek size skin soap

8. since smart speed shame

Written Expression: Giving directions

Write a few sentences to give a person directions to find:

1. the nearest fire station

2. the principal's office at school

Word Families: 'Th' as in 'thank'

The words in the box belong to the same family of sounds.

```
third    theft    thank    thrill    thrash
```

Write new words of the same family from the clues.

1. not fat

2. not thin

3. worn on a foot

4. use your brain

Add a Letter

Make new words by adding the letter **s** to these words. (Do not make it the last letter!)

1. hip   **2.** and   **3.** now   **4.** wet   **5.** trap   **6.** pill

Just For Fun: Homonyms

Copy and complete the puzzles. Each pair of words sound the same but are spelled differently.

 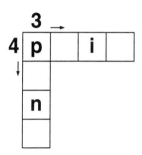 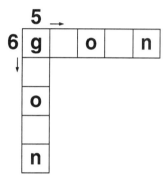

1. a tiny hole in skin   **3.** hurt
2. Will I ____ the tea?   **4.** window glass
5. became large
6. moan

More Fun

Make words with the scrambled letters. The first letter of each word is given to you. Write each word in your notebook.

1. b ____ (ate)   **5.** d ____ (oro)   **9.** c ____ (iyt)
2. l ____ (ona)   **6.** h ____ (tru)   **10.** t ____ (mae)
3. e ____ (hac)   **7.** l ____ (fae)   **11.** f ____ (eir)
4. a ____ (erft)   **8.** l ____ (iad)   **12.** j ____ (edump)

Reading: The odd sound

Write each row of words. Three words in each row have the same vowel. Circle the word that does not belong.

1. soap crow snow gown

2. slow stone shown fowl

3. gown throw foam close

4. rope glow loaf crown

5. round flown clown spout

6. doll roast boat blow

7. slow howl town owl

8. frown growl bowl couch

Word Knowledge: One word instead of two or more

Match each word from the box to its meaning below. Write them in your notebook.

    fewer   breeze   crumbs   change   stare   feast
    wrecked   now   camp   picnic   juice   ceiling

1. at present

2. special rich meal

3. meal outdoors

4. liquid part

5. live in a tent

6. broken beyond repair

7. look hard at

8. roof of a room

9. less than before

10. money left over

11. tiny bits of bread

12. gentle wind

Sentences: Joining with 'and' and using the 's' form of verb

If both sentences to be joined have the **s** form of verb then the verb must be changed.

Joachim **digs** in the sand. Jane **digs** in the sand.
Joachim and Jane **dig** in the sand.

Join the pairs of sentences in the same way.

1. The dog sleeps in the basket. The cat sleeps in the basket.

2. A cow eats grass. A horse eats grass.

3. Allan plays softball. Erica plays softball.

4. Birds eat insects. Frogs eat insects.

5. Dorothy drinks milk. I drink milk.

6. The plane lands here. The helicopter lands here.

Usage: 'Much' or 'many'

We use **many** with objects that can be counted.
We use **much** to express an amount.

We have **many** sheep.   Is there **much** food left?

Use **much** or **many** when you write each sentence.

1. Do not eat too _____ nuts.

2. I ate too _____ spaghetti.

3. There are _____ flowers in her garden.

4. I saw _____ people at the circus.

5. Does she drink _____ coffee?

6. The cook put too _____ salt in the soup.

Grammar: Pronouns

Pronouns are words used instead of the nouns. A pronoun is often used
to replace a noun that is used again in a following sentence.

Jim collects stamps. Jim has an album.
Jim collects stamps. **He** has an album.

Use pronouns from the box in place of the nouns in brackets. Write
each pair of sentences.

> he   her   she   his

1. Vida came to school. She forgot (Vida's) books.

2. Leroy is ill. (Leroy) is in bed.

3. Allan is coming. (Allan) is bringing (Allan's) bat.

4. Marie is eight. (Marie) is very tall.

Dictionary Skills: Words beginning with the same letters

Write each group of words in dictionary order.

1. plant porch piece paste

2. divide danger doctor during

3. wife wear wait wolf

4. enough expect engine either

5. potato plenty pencil partly

6. maid meal more munch

7. twist treat taste thumb

8. health handle hoping hungry

Written Expression: A radio commercial

Write five or more sentences for a radio commercial advertising a type of suit that makes the person wearing it invisible.

Just For Fun: What am I?

Write the answers to the riddles in your notebook.

1. I am round and flat.
   I am black.
   I can slide across ice.
   What am I?

2. I am long.
   I am good to eat.
   I am often eaten at baseball games.
   What am I?

Reading: Categories of words

Read each group of words. Choose a word from the box that names the category. Write each group of words and its category into your notebook.

```
      rivers    buildings    food    snakes    flowers
              shellfish    birds    dishes
```

1. lily daffodil rose pansy

2. saucer plate cup bowl

3. Fraser Credit Ottawa Nile

4. garter rattle grass python

5. crab shrimp clam lobster

6. crow magpie hawk parrot

7. house church cathedral palace

8. pie steak sausage cake

Word Knowledge: Insects

Match each word from the box to its meaning below. Write each word and its meaning in your notebook.

```
      butterfly    sting    thorax    locust    ladybug
   flea    cricket    anthill    bee    moth    termite    larva
```

1. It makes honey.

2. It flies at night.

3. tiny biting insect

4. Wasps can ____.

5. kind of grasshopper

6. grub form of insect

7. It sings in summer.

8. chest of insect

9. Ants live in an ____.

10. It has brightly coloured wings.

11. orange beetle with black spots

12. It eats wood.

Sentences: Joining with 'and' but changing the form of the verb

When two singular nouns are joined with **and** then the form of the verb becomes plural.

Flora goes to school.   Douglas goes to school.
Flora and Douglas **go** to school.

Join each pair of sentences. Change the form of the verb.

1. Lee has black hair. Kim has black hair.

2. Uncle Tim is ill. Aunt Carmela is ill.

3. The dog was hungry. The cat was hungry.

4. A cow has horns. A goat has horns.

5. Melbourne is in Australia. Perth is in Australia.

6. Iron is heavy. Lead is heavy.

Punctuation: Abbreviations

A short form of a word is called an abbreviation. We can use an abbreviation when we write our address.

Street—St.   Road—Rd.   Avenue—Ave.
Boulevard—Blvd.

Write your address using the shorter form. Then write the addresses of two of your friends.

Grammar: More pronouns

Use the pronouns in the box in place of the noun or nouns in brackets. Write each sentence.

```
their    he    her    him    them    they
```

1. (Mayim and Sonya) are going to town.
2. Give (Andrew) his ball.
3. The boys are having (the boys') picnic.
4. Arnold said (Arnold) was taller than I.
5. My clothes were too small so my mother gave (my clothes) away.
6. Eva would not lend (Eva's) bicycle to anyone.

Dictionary Skills: Alphabetical order to the third letter

Write each group of letters in alphabetical order.

1. mos mor mon mol
2. fol for fos foo
3. lam lar lau lan
4. sam sar saf sat
5. alt alo als alr
6. jer jel jea jes
7. dot dom dow dor
8. rum rut rul rud

Written Expression: Finishing a story

Copy and complete the first three sentences. Finish the story by telling what happened. Make up a title for the story.

One day my friend _____ and I were in _____ doing some shopping. We were alone in an elevator going _____. Suddenly the elevator stopped between floors.

Word Families: 'Ay' as in 'pay'

The words in the box belong to the same family of sounds.

pay   play   stay   sway   spray

Write new words of the same family from the clues.

1. Bricks are made from it.

2. donkey's cry

3. used for carrying plates

4. lose one's way

Add a Letter

Make new words by adding the letter **t** to the words below.

1. his   **2.** suck   **3.** hat   **4.** sack   **5.** rust   **6.** act

Just For Fun: Anagrams

Rearrange the letters of the underlined words to make new words.

1. Make <u>team</u> into something we eat.

2. Make <u>peels</u> into something we do in bed.

3. Make <u>bore</u> into a long cloak.

4. Make <u>stab</u> into things used by baseball players.

5. Make <u>east</u> into something we sit on.

6. Make <u>skid</u> into baby goats.

More Fun

Copy each word. Next to it write any smaller words you see in the whole word.

1. track   **4.** raise   **7.** plenty

2. instant   **5.** waste   **8.** space

3. chant   **6.** train   **9.** meat

UNIT 18

Reading: Thinking about advertisements

Read each advertisement carefully. Think about the statements. Write one sentence from each that may not be true.

1. Binky breakfast cereal is sold in your supermarket. Bill Bloggs the famous football player eats Binky every morning. The crisp flakes are made from fresh corn. Binky will make you grow tall and strong.

2. Woofers dog food is made from real meat. Your dog will love eating Woofers. There is no other dog food as good as Woofers. The food is sold in handy tins.

Word Knowledge: Synonyms

Choose words from the box that mean the same as the words below. Write them in your notebook.

> wash   plot   wobbly   din   sick   fix
> feed   smell   cry   dizzy   wet   dangle

1. damp   **5.** plan   **9.** hang

2. launder   **6.** unsteady   **10.** weep

3. eat   **7.** scent   **11.** giddy

4. mend   **8.** noise   **12.** ill

Add a Letter

Make new words by adding the letter l to the words below.

1. side   **2.** ice   **3.** sing   **4.** fat   **5.** wed   **6.** bow

Sentences: Phrases describing nouns and verbs

Complete each sentence by using a phrase from the box. Write each sentence in your notebook. Underline the phrase and circle the word it describes. At the end of the sentence write **N** if the circled word is a noun or **V** if it is a verb.

---
with large paws   on the table   over the wall   from the sky
---

1. The boy threw the ball ____.

2. The bowl ____ was full of fruit.

3. A dog ____ was on the lawn.

4. A bird swooped down ____.

Usage: 'Lend' or 'loan'

We should use **lend** as a verb and **loan** as a noun.

Will you **lend** me a dollar?

He took out a **loan** at the bank.

Use **lend** or **loan** correctly when you write each sentence.

1. Please ____ me your ruler.

2. I can ____ you my bicycle.

3. Dad took a ____ from the bank.

4. May I have a ____ of ten dollars?

5. Ask him to ____ you his atlas.

6. My brother had the ____ of a horse.

Grammar: Making sets of common nouns

Write the first two words of each set. Choose two more common nouns from the box to make a set of four in each example.

---
hen   cheese   arm   wardrobe   chair

duck   chest   yoghurt
---

1. butter cream ____ ____

2. goose turkey ____ ____

3. bed table ____ ____

4. foot neck ____ ____

Dictionary Skills: Alphabetical order to the third letter

Look at the groups of letters in each row. Put each row of letters in alphabetical order.

1. cur   cut   cus   cul
2. bre   bro   bra   bri
3. kil   kit   kis   kid
4. len   les   lee   lev
5. nes   new   nec   neg

6. gon   gol   gos   gor
7. mor   mon   mop   mos
8. pes   ped   per   pet
9. fre   fra   fri   fro
10. qua   qui   que   quo

Written Expression: Opinions for and against

Write two separate headings:

1. Birds should be kept in cages.
2. Birds should not be kept in cages.

Under each heading write at least four sentences to argue each case.

Word Families: 'Ail' as in 'pail'

The words in the box belong to the same family of sounds.

fail   rail   tail   wail   sail

Write new words of the same family from the clues.

1. letters and parcels
2. prison
3. bucket
4. A hammer hits one.

Add a Letter

Make new words by adding the letter **n** to the words below.

1. sip   2. swig   3. set   4. hut   5. wig   6. wet

Just For Fun: Crosswords

Copy and complete the puzzles.

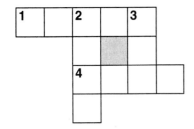

1. opposite to sad
2. a colour
3. opposite to no
4. a bird's home

1. a tiny insect
2. a meal
3. Jack and Jill went up the _____.
4. opposite to short

More Fun

Find the seven vegetables that are hidden in the rectangle. Write them in your notebook. Words run across and down. Each vegetable has five or six letters.

S	B	R	O	K	I	T	S
A	C	A	R	R	O	T	Q
T	E	D	A	M	L	O	U
U	L	I	S	A	R	M	A
R	E	S	A	R	K	A	S
N	R	H	A	R	O	T	H
I	Y	A	M	Y	F	O	G
P	O	T	A	T	O	R	M

Reading: Drawing conclusions

After reading a passage you can decide things about the contents. This is called drawing conclusions. Read this passage, then write the two correct conclusions out of the six below.

> Peter is a giant panda at our local zoo. When he arrived last week from China, he measured one metre long. He will probably grow to one and a half metres. His weight is now about eighty kilograms and he could almost double this in a year or two. He is fed on bamboo shoots, plants, fish and small rodents.

1. Peter is not fully grown.

2. Peter likes being big.

3. Peter is glad that he left China.

4. Peter is not a native of Canada.

5. Peter is a very heavy animal.

6. Peter's favourite food is fish.

Word Knowledge: Antonyms

Choose words from the box that are opposite in meaning to the words below. Write each word and its opposite in your notebook.

```
    light    on    near    together    polite    ahead
  plain    long    pleasant    noisy    never    entrance
```

1. short

2. behind

3. apart

4. fancy

5. far

6. heavy

7. quiet

8. exit

9. rude

10. off

11. nasty

12. always

Sentences: Questions with answers 'yes' or 'no'

Write the questions. Against each one write an answer from the box. Notice that we put a comma after the word **yes** or **no**.

No, some have no poison.   Yes, he learned last summer.
Yes, I was paid yesterday.   Yes, she has a temperature.
No, I am too busy.   No, he has just been fed.

1. Can Brian swim?

2. Are all snakes dangerous?

3. Do you have any money?

4. Is the dog hungry?

5. Will you come with me?

6. Is Angela ill?

Punctuation: Numerals

The winner of a race comes first. The shortened form of the word **first** is written **1st.**

Write the shortened form of the numbers from 1 to 30. For example:

1st   2nd   3rd   4th . . . etc.

Grammar: Verbs that are helpers

Many verbs consist of two words. The first part **be**, or **have** is a helper.

The baby is **crawling**.   The race **has started**.

Write the correct helping word from the brackets when you write each sentence.

1. Rina (has have) lost her ribbon.

2. Robin and Manuel (has have) left school.

3. The bird (has have) eaten the worm.

4. Phillip (is are) throwing stones.

5. He and I (is are) playing marbles.

6. The father of the girl (is are) coming.

Dictionary Skills: Alphabetical order to the third letter

Look at the groups of letters in each row. Put each row of letter in alphabetical order.

1. den dep deg del

2. ful fur fun fus

3. clu cli cle clo

4. hom hol hop hot

5. pre pro pra pri

6. gol gor gon gos

7. enl end ene enc

8. win wip wir wit

9. tar tas tak tam

Written Expression: A book review

Copy and complete the sentences to form a book review.

> I read a book called _____. It was written by _____. The story is about _____. The character I liked best was _____. He/She _____. I enjoyed the part _____.

Word Families: 'Ee' as in 'weed'

The words in the box belong to the same family of sounds.

> bee see weed reef flee

Write new words of the same family from the clues.

1. Elm is one.

2. kind of meat

3. to eat

4. a number

Just For Fun: Homonyms

Copy and complete the puzzles. Each pair of words sound the same but are spelled differently.

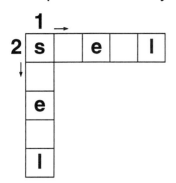

1. made from iron
2. to rob

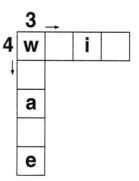

3. cry
4. large sea creature

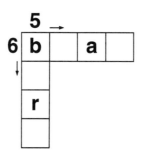

5. animal
6. not clothed

More Fun

Copy this square. Fill in your answers across the square. You will find your answers also read downwards.

Clues

1. place where we live
2. not shut
3. repair
4. finishes

Reading: Finding facts

Petroleum is a dark liquid that comes from the earth. It is sometimes called 'black gold' because it is so valuable. Many things are made from petroleum. One important use is fuel.

The family car and trucks that run across our highways are usually powered by gasoline, which is made from petroleum. In fact most engines, including jets, are driven by fuels made from petroleum. Even oils and greases, called lubricants, are made from this liquid. Without lubricants, engines would not be able to run smoothly.

Petroleum is Canada's major energy source. Most of Canada's petroleum comes from rock beds in Western Canada. In the future, much of Canada's petroleum is expected to come from the seabed off the East Coast, or in the Arctic.

Write the two sentences that are true.

1. Canada has very little petroleum.
2. Cars must use oil to run smoothly.
3. Petroleum is very valuable.
4. Petroleum is also called gasoline.

Word Knowledge: More about the earth

Read the words in the box. Match each word from the box to its meaning below. Write each word and its meaning in your notebook.

```
       ice    lava    lake    diamond    coal    soil
    valley    swamp    desert    creek    plain    jungle
```

1. small stream
2. precious stone
3. wet, soft land
4. inland water
5. frozen water
6. molten rock

7. dry, sandy region
8. land between hills
9. earth for plants
10. land overgrown with trees
11. flat land
12. a black fuel

Sentences: Making two into one by using an adjective

Look at the two sentences below. By changing the verb **was tired** into an adjective **tired**, the two sentences become one. Remember that an adjective goes before a noun.

The dog **was tired**. It lay in the shade.
The **tired** dog lay in the shade.

Change each pair of sentences into one.

1. The laundry was wet. It flapped in the wind.
2. The cat is hungry. It must be fed.
3. The window is broken. It should be fixed.
4. The fruit is ripe. It must be picked.
5. The boy was sick. He went to bed.
6. The girl was clever. She came first.

Usage: The verb 'to be' with not

When using the word **not,** use the correct form of the verb **to be.**
Write these sentences using **am, is** or **are** in the spaces.

1. Jim _____ not tired.
2. I _____ not thirsty.
3. You _____ not watching.
4. They _____ not poor.
5. Fay and Tim _____ not home.

6. I _____ not going.
7. She _____ not stupid.
8. The girls _____ not going skating.
9. I _____ not sleepy.

Grammar: Collective nouns

Collective nouns are words that name groups of people or things.

The **class** sat down.   The **herd** stampeded.

Write the collective nouns. Next to them write the correct common noun
they name from the box.

```
    ships    people    clothes    cards    thieves
          bushes    birds    fish    dishes
```

1. clump
2. fleet
3. set

4. flock
5. gang
6. crowd

7. pack
8. school
9. suit

Dictionary Skills: Alphabetical order to the third letter

Write each group of words in alphabetical order.

1. cheese change choose churn
2. plod plump pliers plenty
3. mouth money month motor
4. felt fern feel feat
5. store stare stiff stunt
6. hoping hound hollow horse

Written Expression: Guess what?

Write a few sentences about two objects found in your classroom. Ask a friend to guess what they are. Don't make them too easy. When you have finished you could try to describe someone in your class, but not your teacher. Can your friend guess who it is?

Add a Letter

Make new words by adding the letter **m** to these words.

1. cap   **2.** pup   **3.** lap   **4.** skim   **5.** clap   **6.** trap

Just For Fun: What am I?

1. I am a pair.
I have wheels.
I fit onto feet.
I am a pair of _____ _____.

2. I am a bright light in the sky.
My shape changes each day.
I shine at night.
I am the _____.

More Fun

Choose **ir, or, ee** and **ur** to complete each word. Write them in your notebook.

1. g _____ l

2. s _____ f

3. f _____ m

4. t _____ f

5. st _____

6. c _____ n

7. d _____ t

8. l _____ d

9. c _____ l

10. kn _____

11. b _____ d

12. t _____ th

13. c _____ d

14. w _____ p

15. b _____ n

16. t _____ n

Reading: Context clues

Read the poem. Some of the words are missing. Choose words from the box to complete the poem.

stare	circus	ten	Frumptious	feet	funny

Frumptious Bren

Twenty toes had Frumptious Bren,
where other people have but ____.
In summer, when his ____ were bare
he noticed people laugh and ____,
and, though at first inclined to frown,
he joined a ____ as a clown.
His feet, that people find so ____
are now how ____ earns his money.

Michael Dugan

Word Knowledge: Similes

A simile is a part of a statement that says one thing is like another. Write each simile below and complete it with a word from the box.

owl	ape	snail	dog
lion	mule	bee	bat	lark

1. as slow as a ____
2. as wise as an ____
3. as busy as a ____
4. as sick as a ____
5. as hairy as an ____

6. as blind as a ____
7. as happy as a ____
8. as stubborn as a ____
9. as brave as a ____

Sentences: Joining with 'when' in the middle

Two simple sentences can be joined to make one longer one by using **when**. We put **when** in front of the part that happens first.

We have to come home. It becomes dark.
We have to come home **when** it becomes dark.

Make one sentence out of each pair by using **when**.

1. The truck came to a stop. The light turned red.
2. The dog barked. He saw the rabbit.
3. I jumped. The door slammed.
4. We put on our raincoats. It started to rain.
5. The door slammed. The wind blew.
6. We all cheered. She scored a goal.

Punctuation: Contractions

We often shorten words when speaking. They are called contractions. An apostrophe is used where one or more letters have been left out. You will notice these words in books where the actual words of a speaker are used.

is not—**isn't**   do not—**don't**   cannot—**can't**

Write each pair of words and next to them write the correct contraction from the box.

> she's   I'll   we'd   it's   I've   she'll

1. it is   **2.** I will   **3.** I have   **4.** she will   **5.** she is   **6.** we had

Grammar: More collective nouns

Write the collective nouns. Next to them write the correct common noun they name from the box.

```
        bees    books    potatoes    cattle    soldiers
            beads    pupils    trees    puppies
```

1. army

2. library

3. hive

4. forest

5. sack

6. class

7. litter

8. string

9. herd

Dictionary Skills: Alphabetical order to the third letter

Write each group of words in alphabetical order.

1. grit gruff grope grace

2. which where what whose

3. truth tried trees trim

4. lose love loft long

5. shock sheet shin shut

6. less lean lend letter

Written Expression: How I came to be

Pretend you are one of the objects below. Tell how you came into the world in your present form and something about your life.

1. packet of butter

2. a table

3. a shoe

Word Families: 'Ea' as in 'peak'

The words in the box belong to the same family of sounds.

```
        pea    leak    peak    teak    read
```

Write new words of the same family from the clues.

1. a drink

2. It grows on a tree.

3. a tiny insect

4. not strong

Just For Fun: Anagrams

Rearrange the letters of each underlined word to make new words.

1. Make <u>read</u> into a word used in letters.

2. Make <u>keen</u> into part of your leg.

3. Make <u>lump</u> into a fruit.

4. Make <u>reed</u> into an animal.

5. Make <u>liars</u> into something a train runs on.

6. Make <u>send</u> into finishes.

More Fun

Each line contains two words that are mixed together. The clues are underneath. Number and write both words.

1. e c l o m w
   (tree and animal)

2. g t i r r r a o f f e u t
   (animal and fish)

3. d r o o n s k e e y
   (animal and flower)

4. m g o o t a h t
   (animal and insect)

5. b m r i e l a k d
   (food and drink)

6. r p a e b a b r i t
   (animal and fruit)

80

Reading: One fact too many

Read the problems carefully. In each one you will find a sentence that is not necessary for finding the answer. Write each unnecessary sentence in your notebook.

1. Mom's appointment with the dentist was at 11 o'clock. She arrived at the dentist's office at 11:30. She was too busy to see her for another ten minutes. What time did Mom see the dentist?

2. Ivan had between 10 and 20 marbles. Half his marbles were red ones. If he counted them by ones he would have more than 11. If he counted them by threes he would have two over. How many marbles did he have?

Word Knowledge: Places where people or creatures live

Number and copy the names of people or creatures. Choose from the box the place where each lives. Write each place next to the creature or person.

```
palace    aviary    convent    prison    stable    barracks
    hive    aquarium    kennel    sty    hutch    shell
```

1. bees	**5.** king	**9.** birds
2. horse	**6.** dog	**10.** fish
3. snail	**7.** soldiers	**11.** nun
4. pig	**8.** rabbit	**12.** convict

Sentences: Joining with 'when' at the beginning

The joining word **when** may be used at the beginning of a sentence. A comma is needed to separate the two parts.

The girl went on a picnic. She saw a raccoon.
When the girl went on a picnic, she saw a raccoon.

Join these pairs of sentences in the same way. Don't forget the comma.

1. The rain stops. We shall play in the yard.
2. The moon shines. You can see at night.
3. I press the button. The light goes on.
4. I eat tomatoes. I get a rash.
5. The wind blows hard. The trees bend.
6. The dog is hungry. He licks his bowl.

Usage: 'Was' or 'were'

Write each sentence. Use **was** or **were** in the blank spaces.

1. _____ you lying in the sun?
2. Indira and Mabel _____ in the car.
3. One cup _____ cracked but several _____ all right.
4. _____ your father on the team?
5. Donald _____ slow but his brothers _____ faster.
6. The leaves of the tree _____ falling.

Grammar: Plural nouns ending in 'sh,' 's' or 'x'

Nouns that end in **sh, s** or **x** form the plural by adding **es**.
In your notebook, write the plural forms of these nouns.

1. one bush   two _____
2. one box   two _____
3. one beach   two _____
4. one gash   two _____
5. one bus   two _____
6. one glass   two _____
7. one mass   two _____
8. one six   two _____
9. one lass   two _____
10. one wish   two _____

Dictionary Skills: Alphabetical order to the third letter

Put each group of words into alphabetical order.

1. river right ripe ride

2. frame fresh fruit friend

3. speed spite spade spoke

4. cloth climb clear clump

5. match march mail mast

6. wolf worm wonder wool

Written Expression: I am a cat

Pretend you are a cat. Complete the story by adding one or more words in the spaces.

I am a ____ cat. You could describe me by saying ____. I live with ____ in a ____. During the day I ____. At night ____. I hate ____.

Word Families: 'ine' as in 'dine'

The words in the box belong to the same family of sounds.

dine   fine   line   vine

Write new words of the same family from the clues.

1. belongs to me

2. a number

3. kind of wood

4. drink made from grapes

Just For Fun: Missing letters

Put in the missing letters. Write the words in your notebook.

__ a __ e __   an animal which travels across the desert

__ __ __ w __   a person who makes us laugh

c __ __ __ __   peaches and ____

__ __ r __ __ __   things grow in it

__ o __ __ __ __   another name for mom

__ i __ __   it breathes through gills

Reading: The odd sound

Write each row of words. Three words in each row have the same vowel sound. Circle the word that does not belong.

1. near year head clear
2. deaf treat dear team
3. meet beak seat bread
4. reap meant dream mean

5. clean tread heap bean
6. peal peel dead seal
7. health bleat beast bean
8. frown growl bowl couch

Word Knowledge: Sports

Match each word in the box to its meaning below. Write each word and its meaning in your notebook.

> baseball   soccer   archery   football   track and field
> rowing   squash   curling   golf   butterfly
> tennis   athletes

1. They play sports.
2. Arrows are used.
3. played with rackets
4. a swimming stroke
5. played with bats
6. played with clubs

7. Players kick goals.
8. Boats are used.
9. played with four walls
10. Rocks and brooms are used.
11. running and jumping
12. Players run with an oval ball.

Sentences: Making a question by moving the verb

When the verb **to be** is used in a simple statement we can make a question by moving that verb. A question mark must come at the end.

He is happy.   Is he happy?

Make questions out of these statements.

1. She is tired.

2. It is soft.

3. I am late.

4. They are coming.

5. He is very hungry.

6. You are thirsty.

7. He can play.

8. We are early.

Punctuation: More contractions

Choose the correct contraction from the box to match each exercise.

```
        you'd    they're    who's    they'll
                 haven't    couldn't
```

1. who is

2. have not

3. could not

4. you had

5. they will

6. they are

Grammar: Matching adjectives

Match each adjective from the box to the noun it describes. Write both words in your notebook.

```
        tall    clever    blunt    fast    stale    ten
                loud    round    raw
```

1. _____ car

2. _____ ball

3. _____ meat

4. _____ bread

5. _____ knife

6. _____ building

7. _____ noise

8. _____ girl

9. _____ toes

Dictionary Skills: Alphabetical order to the fourth letter

Put each group of words into alphabetical order.

1. shame shark shall shape   **3.** trap tray tram train

2. flat flame flap flake   **4.** cram crab crag crash

Written Expression: How to do it

Write four or more sentences describing how to give a dog a bath.

Word Families: 'ied' as in 'tried'

The words in the box belong to the same family of sounds.

> tried   fried   pried   shied

Write new words of the same family from the clues.

1. stopped living   **3.** bound with a rope

2. wept   **4.** said something untrue

Just For Fun: Homonyms

Copy and complete each puzzle. Each pair of words sound the same but are spelled differently.

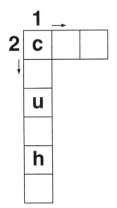

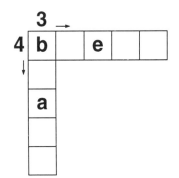

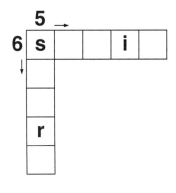

1. a small bed   **3.** come to pieces   **5.** step

2. captured   **4.** used for stopping   **6.** look hard

Reading: Finding details

The emu is the largest Australian bird. Only the ostrich, which lives in Africa, is larger. An emu cannot fly, but its long legs enable it to run fast. This bird lives in open country and feeds on fruits, grass and plant roots. A female lays up to a dozen blue-green eggs. The nest is a shallow hole in the ground. When the baby chicks first hatch they have a striped pattern on their feathers.

Write each sentence. Use a word from the box to fill in the blanks.

```
     striped    meat    blue-green    trees
     grass    red-brown    black    holes
```

1. An emu eats _____.

3. Its eggs are _____.

2. Baby emus are _____.

4. Emus nest in _____.

Word Knowledge: Synonyms

Choose words from the box that mean the same as the words below. Write them in your notebook.

```
     brave    pleasing    bashful    foolish
     awkward    tired    jolly    frightened
     active    slender    gloomy    idle
```

1. attractive

7. sad

2. lively

8. fearless

3. weary

9. scared

4. lazy

10. silly

5. thin

11. shy

6. happy

12. clumsy

Sentences: Joining with 'before'

The word **before** can be used to join two sentences. We put **before** in front of the part that happened second.

> I dug a hole. I planted the tree.
> I dug a hole **before** I planted the tree.

Make each pair of sentences into one by using **before**.

1. I cleaned my teeth. I went to the dentist.

2. The ship came into port. The storm broke.

3. We found some bait. We went fishing.

4. They wanted to reach home. It became dark.

5. The whistle blew. He could score a goal.

Usage: Replacing the word 'nice'

We often write or say the word **nice** when there are better words we could use. Write each sentence using a word from the box instead of **nice**.

```
pleasing    kind    tasty    pretty
      fine    good-natured
```

1. I gave Mom some **nice** flowers for her birthday.

2. That singer has a **nice** voice.

3. We ate a **nice** meal at the cafe.

4. It was a **nice** day for the picnic.

5. Bonzo is a **nice** dog who never bites.

6. The man was **nice** to the stray kitten

Grammar: Plural nouns ending in 'y'

When words end in **y** with a consonant before the **y** we change the **y** to **i** and add **es** to form the plural.

one baby   **two babies**

Copy and complete each exercise below. If a vowel comes before the **y**, simply add **s**.

1. one fly two _____   **6.** one story two _____

2. one key two _____   **7.** one sky two _____

3. one cherry two _____   **8.** one city two _____

4. one lady two _____   **9.** one boy two _____

5. one spy two _____   **10.** one trolley two _____

Dictionary Skills: Alphabetical order to the fourth letter

Put each group of words into alphabetical order.

1. cloth   close   clock   cloak   **3.** plum   plug   plus   plural

2. slam   slap   slat   slab   **4.** floor   flop   flog   flour

Written Expression: Finishing a story

Copy and complete the first two sentences. Finish the story by telling what happened. Make up your own title for the story.

Last summer _____ and I hired a canoe. We were in the middle of _____ when it sprang a leak.

Word Families: 'Eal' as in 'veal'

The words in the box belong to the same family of sounds.

deal   teal   veal   weal   zeal

Write new words of the same family from the clues.

1. dinner or lunch   **3.** not false

2. Bells _____.   **4.** make better

Just For Fun: Crosswords

Copy and complete the puzzles.

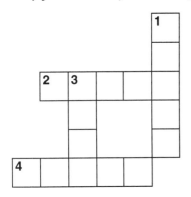

1. a king and _____
2. It's long and it slithers.
3. It's on your face.
4. It's found on the beach.

1. a long hot season of the year
2. like a rat
3. We sleep in it.
4. opposite to brother

More Fun

Here are twelve things we can eat. Every other letter has been left out. Write each item in your notebook.

1. B __ I __ E __   E __ G
2. R __ A __ T   __ E __ F
3. F __ U __ T   __ A __ A __
4. F __ E __ C __   __ R __ __ S
5. A __ P __ E   P __ E
6. P __ R __   C __ O __
7. C __ E __ M   __ H __ E __ E
8. G __ I __ L __ D   __ T __ A __
9. F __ I __ D   __ I __ E
10. H __ T   __ O __
11. F __ S __   A __ D   __ H __ P __
12. P __ E   __ N __   I __ E   __ R __ __ M

Reading: Moods we feel

Read the passage carefully.

Harry was looking forward to his grandparents' visit. His only hobby was skateboarding. His skateboard was stolen last year and he had to be content with borrowing his brother's occasionally. Harry had written to his grandparents about how much he missed having his own skateboard. On the day of his grandparents' arrival, Harry unwrapped his presents. There were some clothes, a pen and pencil set, and tucked into his grandmother's suitcase was a shiny, new skateboard.

Choose a word from the box to complete the first sentence. Use the same word in the second sentence and give your reason.
How did Harry feel?

```
sad    angry    happy
```

1. Harry felt ____ .

2. He felt ____ because ____ .

Word Knowledge: More feelings

Match each word in the box to its meaning below. Write each word and its meaning in your notebook.

```
frightened    cheerful    depressed    timid    amazed
    anxious    furious    thrilled    weary    serene
```

1. calm
2. afraid
3. excited
4. surprised
5. sad

6. glad
7. shy
8. nervous
9. angry
10. tired

Word Knowledge: Sea and river creatures

Match each word in the box to its meaning below. Write each word and its meaning in your notebook.

> sardine   guppy   oyster   eel   whale
> trout   jellyfish   spawn   lobster   gills
> octopus   scales

1. fish like a snake
2. It has claws.
3. speckled river fish
4. It stings swimmers.
5. eggs of fish
6. It lives in a shell.

7. used for breathing
8. largest mammal
9. outer cover of fish
10. It has eight arms.
11. tiny tropical fish
12. small fish sold in tins

Sentences: Joining with 'before'

The word **before** can be used as a joining word at the beginning of a sentence. We put **before** in front of the part that happens second. A comma goes after the first part of the sentence.

> We ate the steak. Sunita cooked it.
> **Before** we ate the steak, Sunita cooked it.

Join these sentences in the same way. Don't forget the comma.

1. I lit the fire. I chopped the wood.
2. She painted the poster. She mixed the paint.
3. He went on holidays. Dad loaded the camera.
4. She went to bed. She read a book.
5. He made a cake. Juan mixed the flour.
6. She laid the bricks. Peggy made cement.

Punctuation: Negative contractions

There are two ways of showing **is not** or **are not** as a contraction.

We're not playing. We **aren't** playing.
He's not here. He **isn't** here.

Write each sentence two different ways using both forms of the contraction.

1. We are not coming.
2. They are not hungry.
3. He is not ready.
4. She is not well
5. You are not listening.
6. It is not too hot.

Grammar: More proper nouns

Write each sentence and put in the correct proper noun from the box.

```
England   Elizabeth   Wednesday   Regina
Canada    July    Toronto   September
```

1. _____ Day occurs in _____.
2. Queen _____ lives in _____.
3. The capital of Saskatchewan is _____.
4. The month before October is _____.
5. Canada's largest city is _____.
6. The day after Tuesday is _____.

Dictionary Skills: Alphabetical order to the fourth letter

Put each group of words into alphabetical order.

1. clap   clam   clasp   clank
2. bring   bright   brick   bribe
3. skin   skid   skip   skit
4. flap   flag   flat   flare

Written Expression: Who am I?

Write descriptions of the work three people do. Ask a friend to guess each occupation. Make the clues difficult by not including obvious words.

Word Families: 'Ain' as in 'drain'

The words in the box belong to the same family of sounds.

```
drain    slain    sprain    strain
```

Write new words of the same family from the clues.

1. not fancy
2. You think with it.
3. It runs on rails.
4. Wheat is a _____.

Just For Fun: Anagrams

Rearrange the letters of each underlined word to make new words.

1. Make mean into hair of a lion.
2. Make loaf into a baby horse.
3. Make late into a story.
4. Make life into a tool.
5. Make salt into opposite of first.
6. Make grab into boast.

More Fun

Copy each word. Next to it write any smaller words you see in the whole word.

1. handle
2. reached
3. dwells
4. stranger
5. however
6. crown

UNIT 26

Reading: A calendar

APRIL

Sun	Mon	Tues	Wed	Thu	Fri	Sat
					1	2
3	4	5	6	7	8	9
10	11	12	13	14	15	16
17	18	19	20	21	22	23
24	25	26	27	28	29	30

Answer the following questions in sentences.

1. What day is April 28?
2. What date is the 2nd Friday in the month?
3. What day is five days after the 18th?
4. What date is the last Thursday in the month?
5. How many days are there in the month?
6. What date is the last Tuesday of the month?

Word Knowledge: Synonyms

Choose words from the box that mean the same as the words below.
Write each word and its meaning in your notebook.

sharp   elderly   trash   crooked   imitate   dizzy
peel   softly   work   slack   hear   edge

1. pointed
2. copy
3. toil
4. giddy
5. loose
6. listen

7. quietly
8. border
9. bent
10. skin
11. old
12. rubbish

Sentences: Questions using 'do' or 'does'

To make a question when the verb is not a form of **to be** we must use a helping verb such as **do** or **does**.

They speak English.   **Do** they speak English?
He plays cards.   **Does** he play cards?

Make questions out of these statements by using the helping word **do** or **does**.

1. The dogs sleep outside.
2. Jasmine likes lettuce.
3. Peter and Michael live near town.
4. The train leaves soon.
5. Your parrot talks.
6. The horses drink here.

Usage: 'Teach' and 'learn'

The word **teach** means to tell facts or give skills to another person. The word **learn** means to receive facts or skills from someone.

Mrs. Gomes will **teach** me to sing.
I will **learn** singing from Mrs. Gomes.

Use **teach** or **learn** in the blank spaces when you write the sentences.

1. Will you _____ me to play tennis?
2. I want to _____ to swim before the summer.
3. Keith will _____ us the new song.
4. Mr. Wen will _____ me at school next year.
5. My brother hopes to _____ to speak French.
6. We can _____ from our mistakes.

Grammar: Sets of common nouns

Choose from the box two nouns which will complete each group of nouns below. Write each completed group in your notebook.

```
pelican   carp   hoe   crow   dish   milk   boot
        tea   thong   saucer   rake   cod
```

1. spade   fork _____ _____

2. sandal   shoe _____ _____

3. cup   plate _____ _____

4. sparrow   magpie _____ _____

5. pickerel   trout _____ _____

6. coffee   lemonade _____ _____

Dictionary Skills: Letters in alphabetical order

Write each group of letters in alphabetical order. Do they make sense? Use each new word in a sentence.

1. nde   **2.** teb   **3.** sfti   **4.** sotl   **5.** oypc

Written Expression: Guess the sport

Write a paragraph describing a game or sport without actually mentioning its name. Ask a friend to guess what sport or game you are writing about.

Word Families: 'Old' as in 'hold'

The words in the box belong to the same family of sounds.

```
hold   told   sold   fold
```

Write new words of the same family from the clues.

1. yellow metal   **3.** brave

2. not young   **4.** not hot

Just For Fun: Compound words

Copy and complete the puzzles.

1.

lhg

2.

iwy

3.

hdm

More Fun

Find the six fruits that are hidden in the square. Write them in your notebook. Words run across and down. Each word has five letters.

P	L	U	G	R	A	P	E
R	P	L	R	A	P	E	N
O	E	O	U	S	P	A	O
O	A	N	M	E	L	O	N
N	C	R	A	B	E	N	T
C	H	A	N	K	E	R	M
F	I	N	G	A	S	T	Y
L	E	M	O	N	A	R	T

Reading: True or false statements

Brer Wolf and Brer Fox thought of a way to catch Brer Rabbit. Brer Fox went home and pretended to be dead. Brer Wolf told Brer Rabbit the sad news. The two animals knew that sooner or later Brer Rabbit would come to Brer Fox's house to see if his enemy was really dead.

This is exactly what happened. Brer Rabbit went into the house. Lying on the bed was Brer Fox—quite still. "That's funny. Brer Fox looks dead, but he does not act dead," said Brer Rabbit. "Dead foxes lift their hind leg and shout 'Wahoo!' to visitors."

Just then, Brer Fox lifted his back leg and shouted, "Wahoo!" Brer Rabbit wasted no time. He ran clean out of the house before Brer Fox could do anything.

Write the three statements that are true.

1. Brer Wolf and Brer Fox were friends.
2. Brer Fox and Brer Rabbit were friends.
3. Brer Fox looked as if he was dead.
4. It was Brer Rabbit that really tricked Brer Fox.
5. Brer Fox did not look as if he was dead.
6. It was Brer Fox that really tricked Brer Rabbit.

Word Knowledge: Antonyms

Choose words from the box that are opposite in meaning to the words below. Write each word and its opposite in your notebook.

> sour   same   begin   more   gradual   many
> friend   most   nearer   sorry   spend   right

1. enemy   **5.** different   **9.** cease

2. sweet   **6.** few   **10.** least

3. sudden   **7.** save   **11.** glad

4. further   **8.** less   **12.** wrong

Sentences: Joining with 'after'

The word **after** is used to join sentences at the beginning or in the middle. It must come in front of the sentence that happens first.

> You may have a swim. You have found your swimsuit.
> You may have a swim **after** you have found your swimsuit.
> **After** you have found your swimsuit, you may have a swim.

Join the first three sentences by using **after** in the middle. Join the last three by using **after** as the first word. Don't forget the commas.

1. You may go out to play. You have finished.

2. He burnt the leaves on the fire. He raked them.

3. The eggs were sorted. They were collected.

4. We had a swim. We lay in the sun.

5. The rain stopped. The boys played soccer.

6. The dentist gave me a needle. He pulled my tooth.

Punctuation: Abbreviated words

Mr. is the abbreviation for Mister, and **Mrs.** is the abbreviation for Mistress. When we write an abbreviation we use a period.

Doctor—Dr.   Private—Pte.   Captain—Capt.
Reverend—Rev.

Rewrite the following. Use abbreviations for the titles and initials for the first names. Leave the surnames written in full. Remember to put periods after initials.

1. Mister Joseph Williams
2. Doctor Lee Chew
3. Captain David Paul Fenton
4. Mistress Odette Cordahy
5. Private Thomas Odynsky
6. Professor Manuela Lopez

Grammar: Matching adjectives

Match each adjective from the box to the noun it describes. Write both in your notebook.

> hairy   fresh   silver   long   clay   handsome
> talented   sparkling   sponge   clever

1. _____ artist
2. _____ road
3. _____ bricks
4. _____ eggs
5. _____ diamonds
6. _____ coins
7. _____ person
8. _____ cake
9. _____ ape
10. _____ student

Written Expression: A dialogue

You have often seen two horses standing together near a fence in a paddock. You may have taken some bread or an apple to feed them. Imagine, as you approached them, that they began talking to each other. Write it down in direct speech. Don't forget to use quotation marks.

Just For Fun: Homonyms

Copy and complete the puzzles. Each pair of words sound the same but are spelled differently.

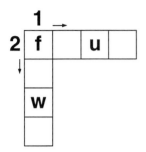

1. dirty or unfair
2. a hen

3. seven days
4. not strong

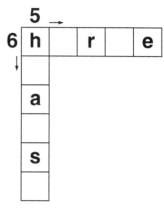

5. farm animal
6. rough voiced

More Fun

Use **aw, ar** and **or** three times each to complete the words. Write them in your notebook.

1. cl _____   4. w _____ m   7. sn _____ t
2. c _____ d   5. w _____ t   8. b _____ l
3. str _____   6. sw _____ m   9. t _____ n

Use **ou, ow** and **oi** three times each to complete the words. Write them in your notebook.

10. t _____ n   11. l _____ d   12. c _____ n
13. t _____ l   14. h _____ l   15. n _____ n
16. p _____ nd   17. fl _____ er   18. b _____ l

UNIT 28

Reading: The odd sound

Write each row of words. Three words in each row have the same vowel sound. Circle the word that does not belong.

1. field leash pearl clean
2. speak chief teach learn
3. here earl pier fear
4. earn thief creak heat

5. bead earth shield greed
6. learn heel heal priest
7. feel meal reach heard
8. meat greet search beach

Word Knowledge: More idioms

Write each sentence and use the correct word from the box.

> leg   cuff   handle   dogs   butter   apple   boat
> lips   time   thumbs   tooth   moon

1. You had better let sleeping _____ lie.
2. We are all in the same _____.
3. She is so good that _____ wouldn't melt in her mouth.
4. Don't fly off the _____.
5. The baby is the _____ of his mother's eye.
6. We fought _____ and nail to win.
7. _____ flies when you're having fun.
8. The secret is safe; my _____ are sealed.
9. He's such a joker; he's always pulling my _____.
10. Josef gave the movie a _____ up.
11. Once in a blue _____ she offers to help.
12. He had no notes but spoke off the _____.

Sentences: Negative questions

Sometimes we use the negative **doesn't** or **don't** when asking a question.

She likes music. **Doesn't** she like music?
They believe in exercise. **Don't** they believe in exercise?

Change these statements into negative questions.

1. The moose eats tender plants.
2. You play on Saturdays.
3. Henry collects stamps.
4. The girls read ghost stories.
5. We go riding today.
6. She climbs mountains.

Usage: 'Loose' and 'lose'

The word **loose** means free. The word **lose** means to suffer a loss.

The dog broke **loose** from its chain.
Do not **lose** the money I have given you.

Write each sentence. Write **loose** or **lose** in the blank spaces.

1. I do not want to _____ my wallet.
2. You can easily _____ money in the sand.
3. We may set the kite _____ in the wind.
4. He wore his tie in a _____ knot.
5. The _____ clamp caused us to _____ our outboard motor.
6. Do not set that savage dog _____ or you will _____ many friends.

Grammar: Verbs ending in 'ed' showing past tense

Time before the present is called **the past**. To show something happened in the past we add **ed** to many verbs.

I **play** now.   I **played** yesterday.

Rewrite each sentence using **ed** to show the past.

1. I (walk) with my dog.
2. We (follow) the trail.
3. She (open) the door.
4. He (borrow) some books.

Verbs that already end in **e** need only the letter **d** to make them past tense. Rewrite each sentence using **d** to show the past.

5. Rico (note) the mistake.

6. I (stroke) my cat.

7. She (like) her present.

8. He (frame) the painting.

Dictionary Skills: Letters in alphabetical order

Write each group of letters in alphabetical order. Do they make sense? Use each new word in a sentence.

1. ybu   **2.** iht   **3.** limf   **4.** olgw   **5.** setb

Written Expression: A Haiku

A Haiku is a short simple form of Japanese poetry. It is written in three lines, the first line having five syllables, the second seven and the third five again. It generally does not rhyme. Read the one below then write one of your own about a butterfly, a puppy or winter.

> We know summer's here
> When crickets chirp in the grass
> And sheep look for shade.

Just For Fun: Word maze

How many words can you find in the word maze? Copy the maze and circle each word that you find. Words go down and across.

b	c	e	t	r	a	p	s
i	a	v	a	t	a	w	m
r	e	d	i	t	q	i	t
d	a	o	l	r	a	t	l
e	t	o	p	e	a	e	y

Reading: Categories of words

Read each group of words. Choose a word from the box that names the category. Write each group of words and its category into your notebook.

> hats   relatives   dogs   transportation   drinks
> occupations   musical instruments   boats

1. firefighter carpenter teacher doctor
2. poodle setter terrier spaniel
3. cap turban beret helmet
4. bus train jet ferry
5. coffee tea milk cocoa
6. uncle grandmother aunt cousin
7. violin trumpet flute piano

Word Knowledge: One word instead of two or more

Match each word from the box to a group of words below. Write them in your notebook.

> hedge   proceed   spray   scald   escape   proud
> dodge   slam   mail   peel   decide   drizzle

1. burn with hot liquid
2. fence of bushes
3. run away from
4. light rain
5. swerve to one side
6. pleased with yourself
7. carry on
8. fine liquid in the air
9. shut with a bang
10. make up one's mind
11. skin of fruit
12. letters and parcels

Sentences: Joining with verbs ending in 'ing'

Two sentences can be joined by changing the second verb.

I saw the car. It backed into the tree.
I saw the car **backing** into the tree.

Join these sentences in the same way.

1. I watched the flames. They burned fiercely.

2. The farmer saw me. I climbed his tree.

3. Jill sat on the horse. She patted its neck.

4. They walked to school. They carried their books.

Punctuation: Using the apostrophe with contractions

The word **no**t may be contracted with **does** to make **doesn't** and with **do** to make **don't**. The apostrophe shows that a letter has been left out. Write these sentences using these contractions.

1. It **does not** count.

2. We **do not** play tennis.

3. She **does not** wear hats.

4. You **do not** need to knock.

5. He **does not** like cucumbers.

6. The battery **does not** work.

Grammar: Using pronouns

Use a pronoun from the box in place of the word or words in brackets. Write the whole sentences.

they   she   he   their   it   her   them

1. (Robert) bought (the tent) yesterday.

2. (The girl) took (the girl's) dog for a walk.

3. (The boys) walked through the woods.

4. The family moved into (the family's) new house and I gave (the family) some flowers.

Dictionary Skills: Words beginning with 'ant'

Look up words in the dictionary that begin with **ant**. Match them with their meanings below.

1. part of a stag's horn

2. song of praise

3. insect's feeler

4. continent of the world

Written Expression: Finishing a story

Copy and complete the first two sentences. Finish the story by telling what happened. Make up your own title for the story.

> Last summer I was fishing in a boat with _____. We were anchored off the beach when a fierce storm _____.

Word Families: 'Ow' as in 'blow'

The words in the box belong to the same family of sounds.

```
        blow    flow    stow    glow    show
```

Write new words of the same family from the clues.

1. It is white and cold.

2. not fast

3. become larger

4. black bird

Just For Fun: Anagrams

Rearrange the letters of each underlined word to make new words.

1. Make <u>wells</u> into grow larger.

2. Make <u>inch</u> into part of your face.

3. Make <u>thus</u> into the opposite of open.

4. Make <u>felt</u> into the opposite of right.

5. Make <u>pins</u> into turn quickly.

6. Make <u>node</u> into finished.

Reading: Finding facts

The moon to us looks about the same size as the sun. It is really much smaller—measuring some three and a half thousand kilometres across the middle. Because it is only about four hundred thousand kilometres away, it appears large enough to hide the face of the sun.

The moon is cold. It has no light of its own. The light we see on a moonlit night is that of the sun shining on the moon. When the moon and the sun are on opposite sides of the earth, we see the whole moon's face. If the moon is between us and the sun we see only a dimly lit moon or we may not see it at all.

Write the two sentences that are true.

1. The sun is larger than the moon.

2. Light from the earth falls on the moon.

3. When we cannot see the moon, it is between the sun and earth.

4. When we see the whole moon, it is between the sun and earth.

Word Knowledge: More about space

Match each word from the box to its meaning below. Write each word and its meaning in your notebook.

```
gravity    eclipse    galaxy    orbit    crater    planet
    astronaut    countdown    capsule    space
            re-entry    astronomy
```

1. passing from sight
2. study of the stars
3. space traveller
4. space vehicle
5. unlimited room around the stars
6. large group of stars

7. bowl-shaped hole
8. path of a planet
9. time before launching
10. force that pulls
11. return to earth's atmosphere
12. body orbiting a star

Sentences: 'Not' makes a negative sentence

By putting the word **not** into a sentence we can change it to mean the opposite. **Not** is a negative word. A sentence with the word **not** in it is a negative one.

Gregor is coming.   Gregor is **not** coming.

Make these statements into negative sentences.

1. Some spiders are dangerous.
2. The birds were eating the seed.
3. I am wearing a hat.
4. I am going to the pictures.
5. The racing cars are going fast.
6. They are coming to the party.
7. Shirley is helping her father.
8. The film is showing.
9. The dogs were chasing the cat.
10. I am tired.

Usage: 'Has' and 'have'

The word **have** is used with the pronouns **I, we, you, they** and **plural nouns**.

> I **have** a mouse. We **have** chickens.
> You **have** black hair. They **have** measles.
> Zebras **have** stripes.

The word **has** is used with the pronouns **he, she, it** and singular nouns.

> He **has** a bike. She **has** a horse. It **has** teeth.
> A bull **has** horns.

Use **has** or **have** when you write these questions.

1. _____ Mikhail eaten the apple?
2. _____ it been raining?
3. _____ we any milk?
4. _____ the birds flown away?
5. _____ the chickens been fed?
6. _____ she been away?
7. _____ you been sleeping?
8. _____ I any clean socks?

Grammar: More collective nouns

Match the collective nouns below with the common nouns in the box. Write each pair.

```
flowers   stairs   tomatoes   sharks   scouts
     insects   sailors   trees   dishes
```

1. swarm
2. troop
3. school
4. crew
5. set
6. flight
7. case
8. grove
9. bunch

Dictionary Skills: Words beginning with 'pet'

Look up words in the dictionary that begin with **pet**. Match them with their meanings below.

1. part of a flower
2. a type of flower
3. small
4. turn into stone

Written Expression: Writing sentences

Write three sentences about each topic. The first two sentences must be statements and the third a question. An example is given for you.

Pigs
Pigs are farm animals. Pigs give us pork and bacon. Do pigs grunt?

1. firefighters   2. the circus   3. monkeys

Just For Fun: Compound words

Copy and complete the puzzles.

1.

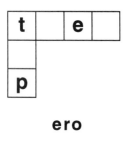

ero

2.

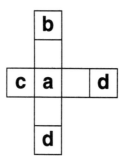

ror

3.

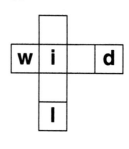

nml

More Fun

Copy each word. Next to it write any smaller words you see in the whole word.

1. history   3. finish   5. together
2. towards   4. fourteen   6. thousand

Reading: Finding details

You have probably seen trained chimpanzees at the zoo or on television. These clever apes can be taught many tricks, including how to walk on two legs. They almost seem human when they drink from cups or peel bananas.

In Africa, where they live naturally, they spend much of their time in the trees. On clear ground they walk on all four legs but sometimes stand erect. If the chimpanzees live near farms they can be pests—raiding sugar-cane or fruit crops.

Chimpanzees range in height from one to one and a half metres. An adult male weighs about fifty kilograms. The female is lighter, seldom weighing more than forty kilograms.

Write each sentence. Use a word from the box to fill the blanks.

> sheep   forty-eight   two   Australia
> sixty-eight   four   fruit   Africa

1. A wild chimpanzee walks on _____ legs.
2. Chimpanzees are natives of _____.
3. Chimpanzees steal _____ from farms.
4. A full grown male could weigh _____ kilograms.

Word Knowledge: More about animals

Match each word from the box to its meaning below. Write each word and its meaning in your notebook.

```
    camel    kangaroo    seal    giraffe    grizzly    crocodile
       gorilla    tiger    elephant    dragon    moose    koala
```

1. eats leaves from gum trees
2. has a trunk
3. type of cat
4. large deer
5. has a pouch and hops
6. animal with flippers

7. kind of ape
8. tallest animal
9. has a hump
10. fierce reptile
11. large bear
12. imaginary animal

Sentences: Using adjectives

Rewrite this passage using your own adjectives in the blank spaces. Can you make it more interesting?

King Midas lived in a _____ palace. He had a _____ wife, a _____ daughter and many servants to wait on him. Yet Midas was not happy. He loved gold and could never have enough of it. One day he was counting money from his _____ chest. A messenger from the gods appeared and granted the king a wish. His wish was that everything he touched be turned to gold. The King began touching everything. His _____ chair became solid gold. His _____ pillows became gold. His _____ flowers in the garden all turned to gold.

Punctuation: Review

Write each sentence with the correct punctuation marks and capital letters.

1. i am going to jeans party in december
2. the red river is in manitoba
3. dont the garbage collectors come on friday

4. she was born on may 8 1975

5. my mother will visit the united states in july

6. is dads hat outside

Grammar: Helping verbs

Write each sentence. Put in the **helping** verb.

1. I found a coin when I _____ walking.

2. Today I _____ going to the supermarket.

3. You must behave well when you _____ visiting your uncle.

4. When I returned the dogs _____ barking.

5. Timon _____ having a party this afternoon.

Dictionary Skills: Alphabetical order

Copy the secret message. Under each letter put the letter that comes before it in the alphabet. You will then break the code and be able to read the message.

u i f   t q z   j t   i f s f

Written Expression: The bucket's story

Pretend that you are the bucket that Jack and Jill carried up the hill. Tell in your own words what happened.

Word Families: 'Oon' as in 'boon'

The words in the box belong to the same family of sounds.

boon   swoon   croon   loon

Write new words of the same samily from the clues.

1. It is in the sky.

2. midday

3. in a short time

4. used for eating

Add a Letter

Make new words by adding the letter **p** to the words below.

1. dam   **2.** ant   **3.** slit   **4.** tram   **5.** ill

Just For Fun: Homonyms

Copy and complete the puzzles. Each pair of words sound the same but are spelled differently.

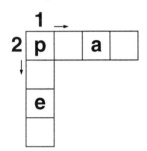

1. Bells _____.

2. We _____ fruit.

3. We _____ clothes.

4. _____ are you going?

5. You comb it.

6. animal like a rabbit

More Fun

Unscramble each set of letters. Write twelve Canadian cities. The first letter of each appears in brackets.

1. N O N T O M C (M)

2. T R I C A V I O (V)

3. T S. ' S O H J N (S. J.)

4. F L I X H A A (H)

5. C R A G L A Y (C)

6. R O T T O O N (T)

7. V O U V E R N A C (V)

8. D R I F T E N O C E R (F)

9. D O N T E M O N (E)

10. T W A A T O (O)

11. G I N N W E P I (W)

12. L O T T O W T E N A R C H (C)

UNIT 32

Reading: The odd sound

Write each row of words. Three words in each row have the same vowel sound. Circle the word that does not belong.

1. pant want bank rank

2. what spat slap snap

3. swam flap clap swap

4. spank squat flat trap

5. span swan plan scan

6. mash dash wash crash

7. match catch latch watch

8. band hand wand grand

Word Knowledge: Action words (verbs)

Write the sentences below. Choose a word from the box to complete each sentence.

> construct   repair   choose   approach   prepare
> relax   stroll   rush

1. To _____ is to walk slowly.

2. To _____ is to mend.

3. To _____ is to take things easy.

4. To _____ is to get ready.

5. To _____ is to select.

6. To _____ is to be in a hurry.

7. To _____ is to build something.

8. To _____ is to come nearer.

Sentences: Using adverbs

Rewrite this passage using your own adverbs in the blank spaces. Can you make it more interesting?

One day Ali Baba was cutting wood. He saw some men _____ riding towards him. Thinking that they might be robbers, he _____ climbed and hid in a tree. The riders stopped by a huge rock. One man, who was their leader, shouted _____ "Open sesame."

A small door in the rock opened _____. Ali Baba watched _____ as the men filed into the cave one by one.

Usage: 'Were,' 'where' and 'wear'

These three words are often confused.

The three boys **were** outside.   Do you know **where** he lives?
She likes to **wear** gloves.

Write the sentences. Use **were, where** or **wear** in the blank spaces.

1. Show him _____ we keep the projector.
2. Did you know _____ the girls _____ hiding?
3. The calves _____ in the shed.
4. Some people _____ wigs.
5. May I _____ these old trousers?
6. She will _____ the new coat.

Grammar: Review

Read each sentence and follow the instruction in each bracket.

1. The bull chased Dora. (Write the common noun.)
2. The cook baked a chocolate cake. (Write the verb.)
3. I went with my father to Hamilton. (Write the proper noun.)
4. Is she going to play with Josette today? (Write the pronoun.)
5. His sister lives with an aunt in West Street. (Write the proper nouns.)
6. They saw some ducks by the side of the road. (Write the plural common noun.)
7. Alicia painted a big picture at school. (Write the adjective.)
8. The baby played happily in the room by himself. (Write the adverb.)
9. The team played football in the park today. (Write the collective noun.)
10. Tam has eaten his lunch already. (Write the verb, which is in two parts.)
11. The dog with black hair raced after our cat. (Write the phrase that describes the dog.)
12. The plane was forced to land in the muddy field. (Write the phrase that tells where the plane landed.)

Dictionary Skills: Words beginning with 'cap'

Look up words in the dictionary that begin with **cap**. Match them with their meanings below.

1. skilful or having ability

2. a short cloak

3. a chief city

4. to upset or overturn

Written Expression: A letter to someone on television

Write a letter to your favourite person on television. Tell him or her why you like the show. Suggest another film or show that this person could do.

Just For Fun: Crosswords

Copy and complete the puzzles.

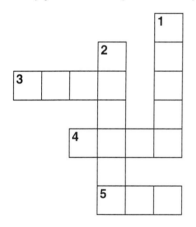

1. A clown is very _____.

2. opposite to rough

3. You bang on it.

4. like a horse

5. opposite to cold

1. something you ride

2. You go there in summer.

3. a baby cat

4. You eat with them.